Birds
Fall Silent *in the*
MECHANICAL Sea

great
weather
for

Birds Fall Silent in the Mechanical Sea
Copyright ©2019 great weather for MEDIA, LLC

Printed in the United States of America

First Edition
ISBN: 978-0-9981440-6-1
Library of Congress Control Number: 2019942653

Editors: Jane Ormerod, Thomas Fucaloro, David Lawton, George Wallace, Mary McLaughlin Slechta

Book design: Jane Ormerod

Cover artwork: Noel Aquino
www.noelaquinoart.com

Photograph of Walter Steding with violin: Alan Rand
Photographs of The Factory: Walter Steding
Self-portrait as Grand Prior of the Lower East Side: Walter Steding
Photograph of Walter Steding and Puma Perl: Donald Sztabnik

great weather for MEDIA, LLC
New York, NY

www.greatweatherformedia.com

Thank you for your support & wonderful Poetry

Birds Fall Silent in the Mechanical Sea

great weather for MEDIA
New York City

CONTENTS

135   Contributors

INTRODUCTION

As real birds disappear from the sky, various species populate this year's anthology like a Greek chorus commenting on mass extinction. Nearly a dozen named species, along with nameless flocks. Too many to count...or not enough? We start with crows.

One for sadness...

In the first crow sighting, "Krahe" (Katharyn Howd Machan), the human perspective is eliminated altogether: "Fox will paint the meadow where/the black crow stalks"; "Smooth crow with gleaming wings/tight and taut and ready/to fly if threatened." This crow is not a hand puppet for the human operator. In a world burning, flooding, hurting, hating, self-destructing...a "mechanical infrastructure/with microphones and cameras" (Jared Smith)...it is something ancient and, depending on your beliefs, possibly magical. An omen. Even a fox can see Facism on the horizon.

Whether or not extinction is uppermost on their minds, our writers seem to share a sense of urgency if not doom. We select from open submissions and it was noted this year that the work, whether poetry or prose, was shorter in length than ever before. There is no waste of time; first lines aim straight for the gut. The opening poem by McKenzie Lynn Tozan is an invitation and, at the same time, a warning: "We are in this together: how we want for/a simple way out: exit strategies."

As in all things human, there is divergence of history and imagination. For some writers extinction looms over the future, for others it is an "old story": genocide, forced migration, domestic abuse, police brutality, gentrification...erasure. A phantom neighborhood reappears in "Titere Ring" (Isa Guzman) where "Ghosts fit loose on the finger/holy broken bodies by a solemn fire/island more than just fragments of memory or imagination." Mira Martin-Parker's "In the Garden of the Consul General" indicts modern civilization for passively accepting a dismemberment accompanied by classical music as trade agreements continue their uninterrupted flow. "Headlong" (Guy Biederman) strips away our differences: we may not have enjoyed the mini bottles or been served by a porter but our fates are entwined on a train racing headlong into a wall.

Almost forgot the other crow. There is something serendipitous about the second sighting in the poem that immediately follows "Krahe." Dan Raphael's "Rained In" begins "So much rain falling" and goes on to report that "The lone crow can't fly in this rain/looking for an overhang to hop to."

Okay, so it's another single crow. And it's raining. And the road beneath the crow is described as "glutinous." But now, without our planning, there are two crows in close proximity...

Two for mirth...

There is joy...and hope...among these pages that persists despite the worst the world can throw at us or we throw at each other. There's jubilation here: Merridawn Duckler's hippie women dancing, the speaker of "Fado Dada" (Valery Oisteanu) whom we gleefully follow to enter seven gates to the delights on the other side. A counterbalance to fatalism may be the works by Tamia Williams and G.G. Silverman where identity and ancestry provide armor and spell. In an interview with Puma Perl, Walter Steding, reflecting on his relationship with Andy Warhol, advises, "Paint your friends; be useful to ones coming up." The final poem, "Zero" (John Paul Davis), concludes that since everything comes from nothing all is not lost: "if you have an empty/page you have everything/...so begin: beautiful,"

Images of nature and myth run through the anthology, and we found these same motifs in the evocative and stunning art of Noel Aquino. His abstract and surreal imagery suggests another language to perhaps answer the silence of the birds. We thank him for providing the perfect painting for the cover.

Update on great weather for MEDIA: On our third trip to the Association of Writers & Writing Programs (AWP) conference held in Portland OR, our editors hosted a panel on collaboration with musician/artist/writer Venus de Mars. Steve Dalachinsky, author of *When Night and Day Become One*, won a silver medal at the IBPA Benjamin Franklin Awards in Poetry, and melissa christine goodrum's new book *something sweet & filled with blood* received high praise from Tyehimaba Jess and Sapphire. From London readings to the New York City Poetry Festival, touring Los Angeles up to Seattle, our community continues to extend.

Don't stop with crows. As you read, count the birds. Step away, count the birds. Vultures, turtle doves, ducks, finches...refill the sky with the sound of your counting...

Nine for silver, ten for gold...

Eleven a secret that will ~~never~~ be told.

MCKENZIE LYNN TOZAN

Exit Strategies

We are in this together: how we want for
a simpler way out:
                    exit strategies,

a blossom lost in a field
of blossoms.
                    (A shadow walks across the moon

and is gone.) Let me speak
for both of us:
                    we want so simply

to be erased: how the hologram
of a humpback whale
                    takes the plunge

into a school gymnasium floor. Its cleanup
is simple:
                    two clicks, and it's gone.

Erase the tanks. Erase our fingers, for they do most
of our bidding. Pull the cloak
                    from the cupboard drawer

and draw it over the edge of
the world. The mess will remain hidden
                    underneath.

ALENA SINGLETON

No Name, No Return Address

If you are reading this   My skin is Black
            And I am being held for ransom
By a brutal monster of a man named Nation

I would ask you to send help   but   spilled blood
and motherless child
            have been crying out for alms for a Mighty long time now
                and I genuinely don't believe that anybody else will be showing up

The bullets at our doors
Want us all to be the last of our name
The lamb's blood on the doorpost
may have kept the angel of the Lord out
but now the devil wants in
And Black skin don't go good   next door   to free-trade coffee
                                and organic greens

The noose around my neck this time
is often called "minimum wage"
        or "police state"
        or "fuck, I can't afford to move again," and yes, for the record,
I've lived in this building for years.

Pressure makes gems
But it also makes earthquakes and volcanoes and fissures and storms
and other things that kill by the millions.
So if you left the kitchen a long time ago & turned your back   I just wanna let you know

that the pot has boiled over
    but the flesh is still on the bones
    and the bones have become angry,
And rightly so.

So you might want to start thinking about
how you would answer to those bones if they came to you for a reckoning
Because they are coming.
And they have questions.

MARIO PONCÉ PAGÁN

3 Conversations

1.

Fog rises from Dyker Heights manhole covers
the rain washes away the cold hours
I roam looking for signs of life
no coquís here
no gallos here
only wet cats searching for meals
meowing in an accent I cannot make out.

I am haunted by childhood memories of Abuela:

Mayo ¿quieres cafe?

Walter Mercado en el radio:

Leo! Tu poder interior te hará vencer obstáculos y salir airoso.
Tus números son:
ocho
siete
cinco
tres

Abuela is still here:

Que el señor te bendiga y te guarde.

Her kisses
the cool agua florida she would dab on my forehead
before I headed out to allá fuera.

Pulled by the craving of Abuela's café, there is no recipe,
I only have recuerdos

of Bustelo y soda crackers from the green can
that later will house the church of arroz Canilla.

Nothing has ever come close to her tacita,
hoy la recuerdo más and it pulls me closer to Puerto Rico

¡Este deseo intenso por pisar tierra santa!
¡Que jodienda!

To settle for what most call home
for what the masses call café.

¡Blasfemia!

2.

I walk looking for some connection to motherland.
"Lejos de tí" plays in the distance.

Crossing 65th street
el coquí dice buenas noches
el gallo canta mi niñez
the sun kisses el Yunque good morning.

Borinquén holds my hands, looks both ways, smiles:

Ok, nene. Puedes cruzar.

En la distancia, Bracetti's flag stands defiant!
Sola, pero brava.

Bodegas these days no longer feel like home
they don't sound like mi tierra.
Bodegas smell like triple soy foam macchiato grandes

Bodegas have been colonized.

I enter,
close my eyes and hear the ocean break on San Juan shores,
hear the tamarindos falling from the trees
el rio
las vacas
the gallinas
Don Otoniel's mangos y Doña Conies' quenepas!

A man holding a Budweiser nods towards the counter.
La doña smiles.

3.

                    Con su permiso, señor
                        ¿le puedo ayudar?

Un cafecito, porfa.

                            Oye Borí y
                    ¿de que parte de la Isla tu eres?

¡Guayanilla!

                    Yo, de Caguas.

She makes my café,
does not stop to ask how I drink it.
Because she knows.

She is a palm tree on Peña Blanca
her smile   blue ocean
morning downpours
kicking up the aroma of tierra

a piece of patria where you least expect it

                    Mijo, aquí tienes tu cafecito.

RICHARD JEFFREY NEWMAN

11

from
This Sentence Is a Metaphor for Bridge

This trespass into verse
will not prepare you;

nor will you find
the strength you'll need

beneath the willow's bough.
The silver wren

singing to its mate
on that bare branch

above the river—
root your resistance there.

Nothing simple solves itself.
Nothing wrecks complacency

like murder. The snow
will grace the ground

beneath your feet
like fine lace

on a wedding gown,
but nothing white

survives the mud.
Within the mud,

lies everything that's true.

DOUGLAS COLE

Drive Through

He wanders up to fast food windows hoping someone will hear his confession. A seagull flaps over his head and he rises in bed almost hitting the ceiling fan. He says, Mexico? Either pelicans or shamans crouch on the river rocks with fright-night movie eyes or maybe his own reflection in the sliding glass as ghostly couples pass matrimonial and erotic and wide-eyed on the next day of the rest of their lives, the lost stepping out of the resort and going back to field basic one before the next bright idea comes along like a pure and simple distraction in a nutshell, and he writes it down as though he has to say stone and stone again in order to have anything to step on because how else are you going to cross a thing like this and how long until you forget you're even saying road and road appears or bed or sleep or a head to rattle around in with that the sky-high primordial face barely out of high school saying, can I take your order? And all he can think to say is, meat. I'll take the meat to go.

ANOINTING OBUH

How Three Turtle Doves Cross Over into Christmas

A fall
down the stairs
          a fight
with the oven door
This is how
          children know their mother is muted
like the colour gray
          Like screams flooded over
by jazz playing on the stereo
          Christmas carols
Our world is too black to snow, in
          -stead we find ourselves
walking through the gates of heaven
          On our mother's face
swollen fat; opening up to let us through.

JULIAN MITHRA

Wormwood *(Artemisia absinthium)*

Mid-March, Ol' Uncle Henry come calling
with an empty flask and full set of teeth,
barking to his nieces to leave off their weaving
and take pity on a dry felon.

Viola, forever plagued by the musical promise
of her namesake,
sang at choir like a flute hewn
from wormy wood.
For her sister's part,
Artemisia looked nothing like a reed,
a rush, a sedge, an herb. She stood
neither tall nor thistle-topped.

When neighbors drained the enclosure
that yearly flooded enough to field
a stand of bulrushes, Artemisia gleaned reeds
for Viola to basket weave.

How could they let him lurch and reel
and *not* offer a biscuit and rum
thimbleful? They may pray
in white-cloaked ardor,
but they couldn't deny a sip
to a hard-luck Uncle.
Once sodden, he shouted.
(Basket whiskers trembled.)

"...and sailor's tobacco!
Women! What good are you to me
or heaven. You packed your wombs
with cornsilk and lead. Only babbles here
come from the kettle. Only coos,
them doves countin' your sins. Would
your Momma faint to see you, and fainted,
you wouldna spare the rum
to revive her soggy bloodsong."

Viola warned Sister away from the scythe.
Hid butcher knives in the wood pile.
Yet. She forgot to steal embroidery shears.
In the fey of night,
beneath half moon's labored breath,
Artemisia snipped a parlsley of the second mugwort.
The one unsuited to flutes and rooves.
The one besmirched by women's floodly ills.
She muttered her version of Gospel of John,
soaked sprig in evil liquor,
mashed its essence with the butt of a pistol.

Morning
brung quick
to Uncle Henry,
rolling off a basket
pile, blathering the doom
to come t'ny cunt not pouring
a draught. Viola's agony fled when
light struck Uncle's unshaved cheeks
and she recognized, among the bulrushes,
a portent of drowning. Artemisa tipped a poison

cup to his lips, like a child. Wiped dribbles from his
chin with the night-pail rag. Weeping at their generous
change of heart, he bleared promises of gold, a new barn,
a second horse, a wood pile towering above the crabapple.

      "So much wood," he raised his hand,

        "take the likes of three women

          and twelve blizzards to bare the ground."

He wheezed; he beat his chest. He looked to their shrinking faces for
a rope, but all frayed. Only sound for next year, when the crushed stems
of reeds collapse to a layer of sod, fit for women scattering seeds far from
home, far from comely recesses of flesh on which nothing but baskets and flutes
do press.

JULEIGH HOWARD-HOBSON

Dream Theory

Eye in a tree with lips. It's got to be
More meaningful than what it is, and why
Is the angel not playing a harp? Wings
Mean that's an angel, right? Or maybe he
Symbolizes all the rock stars that die
While you hold their songs like balloons on strings?

Strawberry means sweetness, or it represents
Women because there are no women in
The artwork, unless the four people are
Not men, which they might not be. They aren't
Necessarily human either. Alien,
Angel, robot, prop? Can you go that far

Without committing? The truck means power,
The ripped parachute means doubt, the road is
Leading you away. From what? Sunset? Bombs?
Perhaps it all means salvation? The hour
Of reckoning comes with skydivers
And two road signs. Let's talk about your moms.

ANIA PAYNE

6 Ways of Looking at a Platypus

A platypus is such a private animal that there is no universally agreed upon plural of "platypus" in English. Some people use the term platypuses. Others say platypodes, platypi, or "a paddle," but these words hardly need to be used.

Once every few months, I search for "online/remote" job postings. I have a faculty position that I enjoy, but I sometimes fantasize about a career that involves fewer human interactions. My fiancé has diagnosed me as an introvert, himself as an extrovert. He can spend hours retelling stories in large groups; I can only handle two or three hours of conversation until I need to make up an excuse to disappear and recharge in solitude. If there was a plural of Ania, it would probably be Ashley or Amy or Andrea; another woman entirely.

The first European scientist to find a platypus' body thought that the animal was a practical joke, something created by an Asian taxidermist who had frankensteined pieces of duck, beaver, and otter bodies together just to confuse naturalists.

In college I unknowingly dated a boy who was bulimic. I was still incredibly naive and not politically correct and hadn't even considered the possibility of male bulimia. After meals, even after lunches in the cafeteria, he'd disappear to the bathroom with a toothbrush. He was Czech; I figured he was being overly cautious of keeping his teeth clean since he didn't have dental insurance in the states, not purging his meals. At the gym he'd hold his breath while he stood on the scale and shifted his weight left and right, balancing the needle perfectly between 150 and 151. Next he'd weigh me and hypothesize about how last night's pizza or this morning's bacon led to my gain of a pound or two. Once every three months he'd go on fasts in order to "test his self control," or so he told me. He was so cunningly charming that he even got two of his friends to join him. A successful fast meant that his body could survive without nutrients; it meant that he could starve for two days while still expecting his brain to ace exams and his loins to give and receive pleasure; all while his skin paled and blotched, his hair thinned. When he finally told me about his disorder three years into our relationship and I expressed total, ignorant shock, his only response was *don't you pay attention to anything?*

In the nineties, Ferrari engineers built a racecar that modeled the platypus physique—stretched oval front, short round body, squat end. Architects thought the style would become popular, but instead the platypus vehicle finds temporary homes at auctions across the world, passed like a mid-life crisis baton. It's currently for sale at $127,000.

For some reason, in graduate school I was attracted to a guy in my cohort who proudly lived in his Volkswagen Vanagon. He only showered once every few days at the school gymnasium and often brought slabs of smoked fish for lunch, which left tangy, moist smells clinging to the otherwise sterile walls of our office hallways. He showed me all of the non-marked hiking trails around Lake Superior, taught me how to make mocha on a camp stove before sunrise, and how to slip my body through the zippered mesh flaps of the van at night without letting any mosquitos inside. If something was modeled after my body it would be the Bialetti mocha maker with its angular curves, holding all of its contents carefully in the bottom of its chambers until enough heat and pressure finally boils the citrus-noted coffee to the top of the pot in uneven, sporadic bursts.

A female platypus is a fierce, self-sufficient mammal. She is pregnant for four weeks, and then incubates her eggs for one week by circling around them, bill to tail, until each egg hatches. Her babies nurse for two months before she leads them to their own riverside independence without ever knowing their father, their mouths still thick and milky with froth.

When I was born, my last name was Payne-Rajan but my mom chopped off my dad's hyphenated surname before I turned two. While she was raising me as a single mother, my mom used to appreciate her brief periods of solitude and counted down the days until I visited my dad during summer or winter breaks. Now that I've been out of the house for ten years and all of her friends in that tiny, dry Arkansas town have either died or moved away, she feels like an isolated liberal living in the Bible Belt. Most of her human interactions now involve conversations with the door-to-door Mormons or the FedEx guy who delivers her monthly wine shipments. She's felt even more isolated there ever since the 2016 election, and frequently tweets things like "How can you stand being you?" to @realDonaldTrump. My mother teaches exclusively online, and her daily phone calls and stories about her conversations with the FedEx man stop me from ever actually applying for one of those "remote" job positions.

Scientists recently discovered that a protein in the platypus mother's milk could help humans break free of antibiotic resistance. A hormone in platypus venom might cure us of type 2 diabetes. For $500, you can purchase stock in Platypus Technologies, a Silicon Valley startup.

I would pay $500 and mine a platypus for a serum that would cure my social anxiety; I'd sip the milk intended for her babies if I knew that milk would feed me the words needed to hold longer conversations without pause, the energy to tell more stories and make more connections.

The early platypus probably had a stomach, but evolution weeded out this organ and any of the genes that could've produced a stomach in future bodies. Molecular biologists want to reverse evolution the platypus, want to prove their knowledge and their body parts essential. In a lab, scientists sketch out ways to bring this dated organ back to the platypus' modern frame. Every day, a platypus eats 20% of its body weight in larvae, shrimp, and yabby and spends twelve of its twenty-four waking hours hunting down these meals; what are humans but 60% liquid?

BILLY CANCEL

talked myself out of this year's UFO Conference

Circuitbendibus right?
invested way too much

through The Wiffle-Waffles 'til   our Cosmic Marker
bombed in THE SUDS. Stella Botch was all

part of it though   we kept going back for
Unstructured Play   i.e. disturbance at-

Frozen Limit-& you mimed- The Net!   thought
x tuning = resonance   resonance x resonance =

time.   Burnt Out Concept plumes of smoke
   still rising from MAYBE NOW the point
to mount a critical response?   outside yellow
rain downs through the orange brown
night making this atmosphere so conducive to
shucking oysters chugging spirits raffling
turkeys   "no

   not that 1" you said "
i'm talking about by

The Old Intercontinental Ballistic Missile Field."

INTERVIEW

It's Happening Right Now

WALTER STEDING IN CONVERSATION WITH PUMA PERL

WALTER STEDING is a musician, visual artist, and former painting assistant to Andy Warhol. A violinist, Steding first played with The Electric Symphony where he developed his own electronic instruments—namely a synthesizer triggered by a biofeedback device that coordinated his music with light-up goggles. He later performed as a soloist at art galleries and at NYC clubs such as CBGB's and Max's Kansas City, opening for bands such as Blondie, Suicide, and The Ramones. He has worked as a recording artist and performer with Blondie, Jim Carroll, David Byrne, Chic, and Robert Fripp. In 1980, he formed his band Walter Steding and The Dragon People and released records on Red Star and Animal Records.

Steding met Andy Warhol at the downtown club Infinity. After speaking with Warhol about his music, Steding was asked to perform at The Factory and he became friends and painting assistant to Warhol from 1980 until the artist's death in 1987. Warhol acted as manager and producer for Steding's music, thus earning Steding the distinction of being one of the only two artists Warhol ever produced—the other being the Velvet Underground.

Steding continues to live and work in New York City. He is a successful painter and has also written, directed, scored, and acted in films and plays including *Polyester*, *Union City*, and *Downtown 81*. He is currently a member of the rock band, Crazy Mary.

Puma Perl: It's fitting that you come from a small town in Pennsylvania named Harmony. Can you tell us about growing up and discovering art and music?

Walter Steding: Actually, I was born in Pittsburgh, and as time went on my parents moved further out into the country. Harmony's about thirty miles north of Pittsburgh—haven't been there in years. I was always an artist. In high school, I was that kid who painted all the windows for Halloween and Christmas. There was an advanced art class and I was the only student in it. My teacher told me, "Walter, stop using up all my paper and go to New York!" So, I knew all about New York from art.

Music was a big influence. I played some violin and piano when I was younger but I wasn't listening to bands. I'd hear them on the radio, but my influences were the avant-garde European artists who were coming here, like Schoenberg. Avant-garde music was changing the 1950's pop formulas, and it became possible to listen to a lot of good music by composers such as Ligeti, Varèse, Stockhausen, and also modern composers like Morton Subotnick.

Puma Perl: When and how did you decide you wanted to come to New York? Was Andy Warhol an inspiration? What were your early years in New York like?

Walter Steding: I always wanted to be in New York. When I arrived here in 1975, I went to the Avant-Garde Festivals that were established by Charlotte Moorman and that got me out of Pittsburgh. Of course, Andy Warhol was an inspiration, coming from the same neighborhood and a similar situation.

Puma Perl: Charlotte Moorman, as I recall, made headlines for playing her cello topless.

Walter Steding: Yes, she was playing her violin underwater and all sorts of things. I started working with a small band—just myself, Michael DeGeorge, and Willard Van De Bogart. We played in the woods with generators and sounds of crickets, natural sound with synthesis and biofeedback devices. We called it the Electric Symphony. It was synergistic conversion. It would change the rate of the sound. I wasn't interested in the science of it and I didn't even care if it worked; I was more interested in the performance.

Puma Perl: Tell us more about how your art, music, avant-garde influences, the Factory, and CBGB's, all came together in those early days.

Walter Steding: I was working with Ronnie Cutrone, helping him at the Factory, and one night Andy came in from CBGB's. I was still playing music at art galleries. He said, "Walter, stop playing the galleries! These clubs are so much more exciting." He'd sat on a chair at CBGB's and it collapsed and he'd found it all exciting. "Forget the art galleries," he said, "go to CBGB's!" And it was wild and crazy. I started opening for Blondie and Suicide, and one day Chris Stein came by the Factory and Marty Thau (music producer, Red Star Records) was there. They said they wanted to make a record with me on it. I told them, "You see what I do. I stand on the stage for eight minutes and I scream and then electrocute myself, and I have this big electrocution machine." They said just show up. So, I went and Chris was there, and Richard Lloyd and Robert Fripp, and what did I know about rock and roll and making records? The only rock and roll song I knew was "Hound Dog," one of my favorite songs and the first song I learned to play.[1]

I was also working on avant-garde songs. I've always tried to incorporate pop with the classical. Philip Glass was an influence. Usually, it's one or the other. Especially now, there's a formula. It's sort of like a haiku, rock and roll; in some ways that's good. It hasn't changed for a long time, it's always a 1-4-5 pattern. There are rules in avant-garde music too, but it's not popular, it's more mathematical. If you turn on the radio or hear muzak in an elevator it's still the same music you've heard from the 1970's when people walked into a station with a suitcase full of money and handed it over to a disc jockey, and said "play my song."

Back when they had medicine shows they always had to have music, someone like Hank Williams playing while they sold their potions. When radio advertisements began, they were able to build these giant amplifiers and antennas and they didn't need the medicine show anymore, they could sell all of their potions through advertising. After the war they needed a way to keep everyone in sync, keep everyone under control. Instead of country and western music here and modern classical in England, they had something called the hit parade and top ten so that everyone's bobbing their head in sync.

"When I have everyone listening to the same tune I will know I have succeeded…" I'm not sure if this is the exact quote but it's by Theodor W. Adorno, a thinker from the Frankfurt School over in Germany. And that's what we've got, like a playlist of ten songs. Now it's in a big state of flux again. How do you get a song heard by everyone?

Puma Perl: That's the question we all ask ourselves! What do you consider your most burning interests?

Walter Steding: Music, art, history. I've been doing these three things all my life. What we don't take into account is life expectancy. By the time you get it figured out, your life is over. Those people who came here in the 1630's are still in charge of this country. They're the elders of the bank, the Federal Reserve, Chase—it's still all the same people. After 1812, that's when there really was a change. America could go to China and trade, and there was money made from selling opium to China. When I arrived in New York, there was a book called *Dope, Inc.* Lyndon Larouche was the first one who really talked about it. Gore Vidal had a couple of history books too. I don't read novels—except I am reading *Portrait of the Artist as a Young Man.* I read it in high school but I don't remember it so I'll probably finish it! Otherwise, I read technical things about history. I take one era—like how the Navy was formed. One thing I'm working on is a twelve-foot-long painting and it's called "America," after the ship called "America" which was one of the first ships they sent to China. For me, it's all tied together—the music, the history, and the paintings.

Puma Perl: Speaking of painting, last year you exhibited at the New York gallery Art on A. This was part of your ongoing project to paint all of your friends. How is that going?

Walter Steding: I'm still working on my portraits of friends. Eugène Delacroix said he only painted his friends, no publicity people, but of course he had good friends like the Pope. Andy Warhol did the opposite. He never painted his friends, only people with popularity. He thought it would not be art if he painted his friends, and it had to be part of his mechanics. Later he told me, "Whatever you do, don't do what I did. Just paint your friends. I wish I had done that."

The Factory, photo by Walter Steding

Puma Perl: What did you think of the recent Warhol exhibit at the Whitney Museum?

Walter Steding: I liked it. It was pretty comprehensive. I was surprised to see some of the old work. I was represented on the video screen; I did some of the music. There were some paintings that I worked on, too.

Puma Perl: We talked about how your music career started in New York. Can we talk a little more about your art work and your early days with Warhol?

Walter Steding: The first thing I did when I came to New York was to work in the Garment District. I was a colorist. Each color had a monetary value. If you were making ladies underwear for Walmart, you'd say go downtown with those colors—make the colors cheap and garish, mix pink next to orange. Only Mother Nature could mix pink and orange! If you were doing something for the department store Bonwit Teller, you'd go uptown with colors. For rich people, you'd use mauve and wealthy colors. If the blue was too bright, I knew exactly how much orange to add so it would be perfectly balanced.

Once Warhol told me that no one could ever match a color perfectly. I said, "Yes I can. I can match any color." He said, "No, even if you use the exact same pink they dry differently." He couldn't believe I matched those colors perfectly, but I did. I'd throw down a length of canvas and he'd say, "Mix up a pretty blue, Walter." He trusted me to make it. I'd mix up blue in a bucket, slide it down to him, and he'd stick his mop in it and swish the paint all around it. He insisted on doing all of his own painting.

The Factory, photo by Walter Steding

Puma Perl: Where were you living at the time?

Walter Steding: I was living across the street, right near Union Square, in one of those great buildings that artists lived in at the time, with full skylights. I pretty much lived just in storage places, you'd bribe someone for the overnight key. I never asked for anything from Andy but I always thought he was generous. He gave away prints and different things for Christmas.

We'd have lunches—the Shah of Iran would come by and eat lunch. Meanwhile Andy would be looking for a comic book he misplaced because there might be an idea in it, while I was being conversational.

Puma Perl: Back in 2010, at a Cooper Union event, Patti Smith advised emerging artists not to come to New York, which she described as "closed off to the young and the struggling." She suggested they find other cities, like Poughkeepsie or Detroit. Do you agree with her?

Walter Steding: No! New York was always expensive. You have to figure out some way to change the world. After Edo Bertoglio made the film *Downtown 81*, we made *Face Addict* together in 2005.[2] *Face Addict* starts where Jean-Michel Basquiat and *Downtown 81* leave off, with me peeling a face away to reveal Basquiat's tags. At the end of the film, people would ask why can't it be like that for us today? All those abandoned buildings in Alphabet City gone. Back then if someone wanted to start an art gallery, they started an art gallery. If someone wanted to make a film, you'd get a camera, get your friend to get you some film, and they'd make a film.

You have to have a base, you have to have a home, and that's what I'm working on in the Lower East Side. When you walk into the Met, you walk up the steps and etched into the marble on the side is the name of a baron whose kid got to have a show on the roof. Don't try that at home, kids. Don't think you're coming to New York and you're going to have a rooftop show at the Met, not without your parents' name etched into marble. The day of a Warhol coming and trying to make it with nothing to go on are over, and even he got so many doors slammed in his face. There's no place to live, no place to rent, without a studio for three grand—but somehow there's still got to be a way. I'm really old so I go back to the days of living on couches, living in storage spaces, but there's still got to be a way.

Puma Perl: What keeps you going?

Walter Steding: Every now and then I sell a painting, but it's really about surviving day to day or week to week. That's why I am the Grand Prior of the Lower East Side! All these secret societies have a Grand Prior. America didn't have something called the Royal Arch. When the English came they were able to elect George Washington president of the new country. The Freemasons, the Knights Templars of the Royal Arch—they are monied men, arms dealers, bankers, and they have secret codes and societies. And these secret societies have their emblems and little Cub Scout organizations, but they're not Cub Scouts—they're 33rd degree masons, senators, and military generals. These are the people who tell the other people to jump. You'd much rather have me! I belong to the Royal Society of the Lower East Side and my parents did not arrive in the Winthrop Flotilla of 1630.

Puma Perl: An ongoing conversation is about how New York is dead. What do you think? Is New York City dead?

Walter Steding: I wouldn't be able to answer that so well because certainly my world isn't dead. I'm out all the time. When people ask me what about our world, here it is, it's happening right now. You just don't see it, but someplace in the city something really exciting, some new explosion of creativity, is happening. I'm being very optimistic, but people were very pessimistic about the fifties and the sixties and every other time there was an explosion. I don't have a specific answer but every night I go out and I hear people talking and I see people working. After World War ll, you couldn't make a figurative drawing, everything had to be abstract. You especially couldn't do the art of the Germans or Russians with beefy women cutting wheat and stuff like that. You had to have Jackson Pollock throwing paint on the floor, then the next guy throws some paint on the wall or some stuff on the floor. It goes from Pollack to Rauschenberg to Rothko, and next thing is it goes down the drain. But at least people like Burroughs and other writers embraced each new generation. Film is a very good example, too. You need hundreds of millions of dollars to make a film for the theaters. That's not going to stop anyone from making films. It's probably going to cause lots of people to make cheap films or images.

It used to take a long time to make a photograph, time to expose it, time to develop it, and now we snap an instant picture, instant movies. It's not going to be very long before you have 3D pictures instantly. And I'm doing big paintings now. I want to be able to be useful. The Howl Happening art gallery plans to help me, and playing in the amazing band Crazy Mary keeps me active with music.

Puma Perl: Any final thoughts you would like to leave us with, Walter?

Walter Steding: The wealth that came to America in the seventeenth century remains. And wages of labor remain the same. By the time we figure it out, we pass on. You can't move ahead just by your own experience. I hope I can break that chain by the work I've already done so that others can learn from it and so that I can be useful.

* * *

[1] *"Hound Dog" was released as a single in 1979, with guitar by Robert Fripp, and is included on the 1980 Chris Stein produced album* Walter Steding.

[2] Downtown 81 *(aka* New York Beat Movie) *was shot in 1980-1981 and finally released in 2000. It captures a day in the life of a young NYC artist, Jean-Michel Basquiat, wandering the streets and clubs as he attempts to sell a painting. The film features artists including Walter Steding, Fab Five Freddy, Kid Creole and the Coconuts, James White, and Debbie Harry.* Face Addict *(2005) tells the story of the seventies and early eighties New York artistic community through reminiscence and original footage.*

Walter Steding and Puma Perl at Howl Happening

PUMA PERL is a writer/performer and is the author of four solo poetry collections, including *Retrograde* (great weather for MEDIA, 2014). A fifth will be published by Beyond Baroque Press in 2019. Since 2012, she's produced Puma Perl's Pandemonium, which merges spoken word with rock and roll, and she performs regularly with her band. She's received three awards from the New York Press Association in recognition of her journalism as well as the 2016 Acker Award in the category of writing.

OLIVER BAER

87

Things will be better when we're back in the city.
Your sisters will weave through loopholes in society
Your uncle will put his gun away
We will not talk about the child in the cherry orchard
Seagulls scream ahead of our arrival
We will no longer lose ourselves to minor pleasures
We will float through the urban landscape
Brilliant creatures bleached clean of idleness
Our needs bled into parlors
Last light travels to meet us
Gunshot speed as it is mentioned
A seagull lying in our path
Silences our trial
A clinical verdict of emptiness
Filling us up with obligatory lies
Rewriting our return to infinite regress
A play within a play within a play within…
A mirror hell lost to despair
Setting a sun, the color of a dreadful penny,
We walk towards the unattainable.

CHRISTOPHER LUNA

Lost Highway

there is a quiet
in these long hallways
that fogs the atmosphere
            like death
the stench of decomposing flesh
and the ghosts of countless lodgers
who exploited the liminality
of temporary dwelling-places
allowed the mask to fall
and enjoyed a newfound freedom
only anonymity affords

history holed up at home
enemies and victims
safely out of reach
they trashed these rooms
            —and a life or two—
simply because they could
fucked the forbidden
ingested the ill-advised
embodied the Shadow
if only for one
            unfettered evening

nearly all that transpires
behind these doors
remains secret

like the vague memory
of transgressions explored
in the recesses of dreamscape

no one looking
no one judging
no one to stop you
from having your way

DEMISTY D. BELLINGER

Paul Gauguin's Woman with a Flower

This white man
He watches us
He makes us with
Brushes, he calls them
He stares at us and
Touches us
He takes us and makes
Us all brown, even
The whites in our eyes
He makes us his
He watches us
He gives us
Clothes like his
He dresses and undresses
Us, this white man,
He tells us
That we are true
That we are nature
This white man
He tells us we're
Before him, says we're
Primitive
Even though
We're right there
With him.

TAMIA WILLIAMS

I'd Rather Have Weeds

Under the harsh but nurturing sun, the gardener wields his timeless scythe along the tops of plant beds, hitting the sunflowers and skipping the daisies in his own perception of beauty like prophetic Apollo who believes in his own visions and versions that tell the difference between grace and grass. I once believed my African hair had to be flowers.

They're rooted. Brown lines birthed from my brown dirt, smooth but furry top-side with moisture deep within. The roots dig in, clutching at the inner-skin, tall. thick. deep. My curls hold strong. Un-uprootable. This trait of clawing...refusing to relinquish its hold on the African dirt, clawing its way to the top on American soil...caused hints of pain as Mother pushed the purple wide-toothed comb in to straighten...to assimilate... the unbending strands.

Yet flowers are picked so easily. Roses have those gentle curves, long half-circles that become the Muse for centuries of lovers. They call my plants haggardly, brown roots in brown skin sheltering brown eyes and an uneven grin. Twisting and turning and bulking and circling, these dancers. Flippant and proud, no average ballerina. No, my afro hair swats to the sound of drums, the beat that balks at bouncing ballerinas, but boos and bruises green the brown skin with the pull of a sharp comb. Your supposed beauty brightens...frightens...in the face of my nappy strength.

My curls are weeds.

Weeds that resist your blades. You slash at me...*blackie...ugly ghetto...black trash...* with eyes switchblade sharp. Out of your so-called friendly curiosity, you ask to touch my identity. You push those painted claws through, invading with all five fingers, and you make a face.

Nose notching north, nitpicking and nullifying my nappy, non-needle pin knots.
Irises iridescent in indigo indignation impeach my cinnamon eyes.
Guffawing gauzily
Gloatingly

Against amber armor.

You try to pass all five fingers through my curls through my scalpmindheartspirit. But my curls bunch. Those winding, overlapping weeds that sway to avoid your attacks, slip unharmed between your gnashing teeth, unwanted but there unaccepted but there succeeding and there.

Those curled brownblackweaved afroed airbags tumbled on the ships and bounced against the whips and marched streets linked by hardy grips. Those weeds continue to stand tall, feeding from the sun you claim to be yours alone and making it their own, timeless scythe shaking the stems but never uplifting the roots.

RICO FREDERICK

These Bones Break Bread

It is nine am + my country is awake with murder,
the dishware in the cabinets agitate
as the two train grumbles heavy underfoot,
house not home sweet stumble drunk on the amnesia
of glass ceiling built luxury from back lashed labor,
e'rethg moves irresponsibly of itself,
e'rethg must die
intractable the skin, blk
makes mama's chil' coffin promised
DOA over MFA, simple ngh-nometry:
majesty + equality =

....

> They love you then whiteout over blk blot
> this America is an abusive landlord
> screaming—motherfucker time to go.

....

If we all went blind who but who would accuse
the Ebonics in my voice of tryinah'
job interview my way into safety.
E're thought in my head wages civil unrest +
the blkest thing I was made to do is
live in Brooklyn for a higher education
which could still
cost me
my life without saying

a word.

TATYANA MURADOV

РОДИНА (MOTHERLAND)

I remember grass here actually being greener.
I remember being drunk,
smelling like campfire,
impressionable and full of impressions.
Nights I didn't quite make it home.
I remember swimming in the cold & deep.
The thrill of it.
How you weren't quite sure if you'd come up.
Swimming out into the middle of the lake belly up
floating
ears submerged
listening to the music of the dark below.
Inhale, dive,
come up to a world covered in glitter.
Someone on shore calling my name,
but I swim out even further.
Even then I was looking for magic.
Slippery bodies and sun.
Goosebumps and salami sandwiches.
Coming up for breath only 'cause you had to.
Playing cards until the skin on your shoulders crisped golden.
Laughter,
so much of it, it hurt.
My wet eyelashes,
he separates them with his tongue.
I had short hair then.

He grabbed it and said I was beautiful.
And it was easier then to believe,
when the nights were so black
you caught glimpses of galaxies.
I remember the smell of it all.
The blooming and burning,
the mix of birch and berries,
ashes and fresh rain.
You ask me to explain to you what this place means to me.

There are memories
and then there's home.
And then there's the place where you want your ashes spread.

NGOMA HILL

USDA Certified Nutracide

It's dangerous amongst the meat eaters
devourers of ground dead cow carcass
smelling fried blood boiled in oil
medium rare they babble
stupid cow eaters
intestines reeking of garbage
garbage cans for stomachs
crying help me, help me
save me from dis ease
food is eating me, food is eating me
flesh consumption constipation
karma crying colon cancer candidate
with a date for the cemetery
money can't save you
oh conspicuous victim of
consumer killture disguised as culture
eaters of unborn chicken fetus
pig carcass on the side
you can't hide
breakfast may kill you
faster than AZT which is
deadlier than HIV
faster than the PBA[1]
and their motto
kill-a-nigga-a-day

supermarket refugee—you can't hide
we charge you with genocide
blood sucking causes insanity
remember you are what you eat beef tongue—pig feet
red dye cancerous
USDA certified the government lied
call yourself a hot dog
slowly dying like a hog
color me an anti-commercial
for the meat industry

---

[1]Police Benevolent Association

AMY HOLMAN

No One There

This was before the house we had went up in flames
on that refuge in the dunes on the barrier isle
and when I could not be more than wind

rattling the screened door to my friends' house.
I played each day with the youngest two across from us,
which was long before the house we had went up in flames

in an unsolved crime of real estate envy, struck mid-
winter when no one was there. Why so shy? I can't say.
That I could not be more than wind

still rattles me. A voice—older sibling, too lazy
to descend—calls down, Who's there? I can't say, too shy.
This was before the house we had went up in flames

in an unkempt and belittling blaze brazen between
the wetlands and the vast Atlantic with its softening air.
And how could I be not more than wind

knocking, I ask my child self who persevered and
still got trapped waiting awhile until I was seen.
This was before it all went up in flames
and when I could not be more than wind.

SARAH SARAI

Dashing Maxim

I dreamt I was…
            —Daphne DuMaurier

It is a sad thing, being a toaster-thin
slice of Pepperidge Farm bread.
But if that is your lot sleep so your
dreams are a roadster zig-
zagging the Riviera.

Had Mrs. de Winter
more adequately
buttered her bread
she might have been
more jolly.

Did you know Dame Judith Anderson won a Tony?
That was later.

In fairness to toaster-thin slices and
unnamed narrators, anyone can drown if
shot by her husband in a boat leaky as a butler let go.

Imagined inadequacies always drag us under.
Time to reckon with wishful thinking.

Is it too modern to ask why these women
didn't leave for America where the national
dream is *to be buttered*, and our motto,
            lonely, yes, but golden, so golden.

AIMEE HERMAN

down in the south where they take parts
of you away

I went to Ft Lauderdale for an erasure. It is easy enough to forego inquiry from others when you choose to remove parts of yourself during the time of year many people go south for a reprieve from Winter. Most people assumed sunbathing, Miami clubs, and the ability to wear tank tops in December. I eased into that assumption. Everyone wants to ask how you are doing, but no one wants to actually hear the answer.

I learned what Marlory did from the internet. I had spent an afternoon with a box cutter to my left and hoarded pain pills from my mother to my right in search of another way to live. She did not pop up right away. I had to get to the eleventh or twelfth search page, then finally found her website at the bottom.

Marlory still had an AOL email and, after reading her very brief mission statement, I sent her a message right away.

Marlory's Erasures Mission Statement:
    We are ███████ a BOOM in ██████ surgery. Botox is ██████████. Breasts and chins ███████. Are you unhappy with ██████████ cannot be cut-up?
I will find what █████████ erase it away.–Marlory, QE (Qualified Erasurer)

There was one testimonial by someone named Lesta.

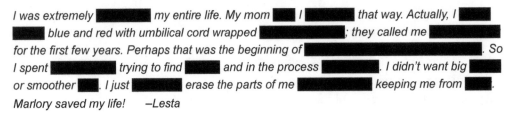

I was extremely ████████ *my entire life. My mom* ████ *I* ████████ *that way. Actually, I* ████
████ *blue and red with umbilical cord wrapped* ██████████*; they called me* ████████
for the first few years. Perhaps that was the beginning of ████████████████*. So*
I spent ██████████ *trying to find* ██████ *and in the process* ████████*. I didn't want big* ████
or smoother ████*. I just* ████████ *erase the parts of me* ████████ *keeping me from* ████*.*
Marlory saved my life!   –Lesta

Strangely, there was no **ABOUT ME** on the site to learn more about Marlory. She didn't even have a last name I could google. After staring at her not-quite garish, outdated site, I noticed a tiny **FAQ** at the bottom, so I clicked.

FAQ

What is this?

Erasure is ▮▮▮▮▮▮▮ take away the ▮▮▮▮▮▮▮▮▮▮▮▮▮ haunting ▮▮▮ ▮▮▮▮▮▮ you, ▮▮▮▮▮▮▮ from living.

How do I?

▮▮▮▮▮ in Ft Lauderale, FL ▮▮▮▮▮▮▮▮▮▮ brick building ▮▮▮▮▮▮▮. ▮▮▮▮ ring the bell first.

The cost?

We do not accept insurance.

I find it interesting what we gloss over. I never questioned that the letters after her name excluded any reference to a medical license. Something about her minimalistic, extremely outdated website drew me in. She wasn't trying to show off. It's like she was just waiting for me to find her. I did not exactly know what she did or how she did it, but I barely cared. I was, once again, moments away from killing myself. The thought of living like this, of being me felt exhausting. I would try anything.

On the week before I was set to leave, my car died. I was driving down Franklin Avenue and a pothole tore open my car's exposed organs—or something more mechanical that I can't remember—and basically totaled it. Imagine if bodies totaled as easily as automobiles. We are flung to the ground, beaten, pneumonia'd and then when taken to the ~~mechanic~~ doctor, they tell us we are done. Basically, the cost of "fixing us" is more than we are worth.

It was too late to purchase a plane ticket or at least that is what my bank account told me. So, I reached out to my friend Sally, who is like a pharmacist but she is really just an office manager for a swimming pool company. Sally kindly lent me her car and I drove from New York to Florida in two and a half days with several stops in between to do human stuff like eat, pee, sleep, and check out South of the Border.

Lizards were the first thing I noticed when I arrived in Florida. So tiny, blending in with whatever they slide on. The lizards were mostly brown like the color of the fence in our backyard that Dad would paint every three years because Maine's Winter would strip each coat away.

In my neighborhood, the pigeons and rats and squirrels and constantly multiplying black, plastic bodega bags all populate the streets. They feel less like wildlife and more like neighbors squatting on the sidewalk for free food scraps or spontaneous bursts of wind lifting them toward a new corner.

I'm not a fan of winter but going south for warmth feels uncomfortable too. Autumn is my favorite season, where the weather can be moody and unapologetically patchy. Or maybe I like feeling unease, not knowing how to dress, what to eat, as the trees let go of what shaded us for months. Maybe I like the end of things.

After my initial email to Marlory, I waited and waited for a response. When I had forgotten all about it, I saw her name pop up in my email.

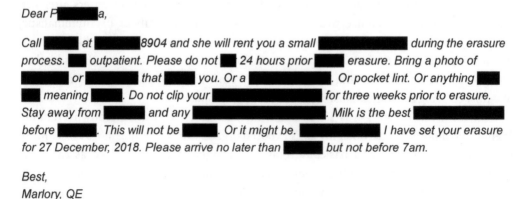

Dear P████a,

Call ████ at ████8904 and she will rent you a small ██████████ during the erasure process. ██ outpatient. Please do not ██ 24 hours prior ████ erasure. Bring a photo of ████████ or ██████ that ████ you. Or a ████████████. Or pocket lint. Or anything ████ ████ meaning ████. Do not clip your ████████████ for three weeks prior to erasure. Stay away from ██████ and any ████████████████. Milk is the best ████████████ before ██████. This will not be ██████. Or it might be. ████████████ I have set your erasure for 27 December, 2018. Please arrive no later than ██████ but not before 7am.

Best,
Marlory, QE

I pressed my suitcase against the wooden floorboards. The cottage I was renting was more like a square with other shapes inside of it: rectangular bed, ovular blue chair that swiveled, circular table to eat things on. There wasn't much of a kitchen, but I'm not much of a cook, so there wasn't much to mourn about that.

The bathroom had a parade of ants walking up and down the porcelain sink. I thought about killing them, then decided to leave them alone. I was only a guest.

I had a few hours left to eat before I was supposed to leave myself empty for the erasure. I kept clicking on the **FAQ** on Marlory's website to see if there were any words I had missed. How does she erase? What if she erases the wrong parts? Is there a process of unerasure?

At night, I slept against the Floridian silence. It felt itchy against my skin. I was too accustomed to the thick energy of sirens, traffic, city life outside my windows. How can stillness be so deafening?

The next morning, I yearned for my routine breakfast of coffee, marijuana and dry toast. Instead, I said goodbye to the carnival of ants still roaming in the bathroom, grabbed the photograph of a bench I used to sit on when I was young enough to be still that long, and headed out.

Marlory's office was in a strip mall which included a nail salon, Chinese restaurant, and gun shop. I parked Sally's car, took a swarm of deep breaths and walked in.

The office was non-descript although what does that even mean? It was almost like her office had been erased. There were no emotionless paintings on the walls as is often the case in places like this. There wasn't even music playing like Top 40 or classic rock or even instrumental. Everything seemed very…well…deleted. I was prompted by a woman behind a desk to sign in and then fill out some forms.

I pressed the clipboard holding several sheets of paper to my lap and began filling it in. While I was expecting typical medical history inquiry, the questions were a little more obscure:

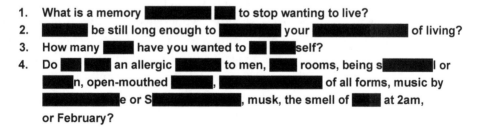

1. What is a memory ██████ ██ to stop wanting to live?
2. ██████ be still long enough to ███████ your ██████████ of living?
3. How many ████ have you wanted to ██ ███self?
4. Do ██ ███ an allergic █████ to men, ███ rooms, being s███████l or ████n, open-mouthed ██████, █████████████ of all forms, music by ████████e or S███████████, musk, the smell of ████ at 2am, or February?

55

After painstakingly filling out each form, the erasure procedure I was about to have was starting to feel less blurry. How odd that when information is removed, the main idea and guts of something suddenly makes more sense.

Being that there was no clock in the room and, per instructions, I had no time piece on my person, I had no idea what time it was or even how long I had been waiting. Then, as though she could sense my slight impatience, Marlory greeted me.

"You must be P████████. I'm Marlory, but ██ p████ly deduced that," Marlory reached out her hand to shake mine. Her grip was firm like she was trying to assess how many bones I had and their force. When she let go, I could still feel the haunt of her squeeze. "I trust ████ consumed nothing since ██████? How about ███, did you drink some, was it ████████? Do you have any questions?" Marlory didn't even wait for me to answer before saying, "OK, then. Let's get you prepared."

Marlory walked me back to a room and instructed me to take everything off. "Y██ ██ put thi████ on. I'll give you some █████y and then come back. Please take out your li██████, to help ██████████████s erasing."

As I removed all my clothes, I thought about what else I was removing. All of my memories—easily remembered and what I've stuffed so far up inside me I can barely pronounce—are what led me here to this unremarkable office offering extraordinary possibilities. I almost didn't even care how she erased parts of me. All I wanted was to be able to live with myself without all this pain, without jumping every time I smelled a cologne that was once worn by someone who tore me open. I wanted to be able to wake up without feeling like my entire body was slurred, not because of a hangover (I stopped drinking years ago) but because my mind and body had become out of focus. It's like my entire body needed glasses and maybe this erasure would help refocus.

The previous night, I had gotten a slightly cryptic email message from Marlory reminding me (though I don't recall a first mention) to list everything that needed erasing and how to list it. I guess I just figured as a Qualified Erasurer, she would just know. That is, I wouldn't have to actually spell it out. However, I drove all these miles and didn't want to risk anything going wrong, so after my meal of fried ramen noodles, broccoli and milk, which Marlory insisted I drink, I had begun my list.

After a few minutes, Marlory knocked and then came in. I hadn't really noticed before, but she was quite beautiful. Almost uncomfortably so. But not in any conventional way. I remember reading an article awhile back about symmetry and its connection to how we see and define beauty. My mother always told me that my eyes were too close together, which was why I (according to her) never looked good in glasses. So, I squint and live life never actually seeing things as they are. Marlory's beauty had nothing to with the proportion of her features. No, it was more about *how* she looked rather than *what* she looked like. Kind of like how babies look: expressions of openness rather than disdain.

"So, here you are. You understand how ███████." She said this as a statement, though I feel like it should have been a question and I just stared back and bit my bottom lip. "There is no ███, well, ████████ compared to what brought ████ on. Use that ██████ ███ scale. I cannot tell you how long ████████ and ██████ recovery ██████████████ or if ████████████." The last part brought on a thick knot in my stomach. I drove all this way and there was a chance I would be no better than before?

"Can I...can I talk to you about my list? I followed your instructions, but I don't know. Should I have typed it? I didn't...will all of it be erased?"

Marlory just stared at me. Her eyes were a shade of brown that made them no longer brown. I shifted in the seat and felt like a musical instrument. The paper gown kept crinkling and shifting against the fabric of the chair. I handed her my list.

She read it out loud:

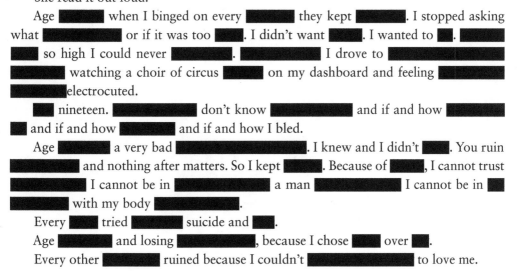

Age ██████ when I binged on every ██████ they kept ████████. I stopped asking what ██████████ or if it was too ████. I didn't want ████. I wanted to ██. ██████ ████ so high I could never █████████. █████████████ I drove to ██████████████ ████████ watching a choir of circus ██████ on my dashboard and feeling ████████ ████████electrocuted.

███ nineteen. █████████████ don't know ████████████ and if and how ████████ ██ and if and how ████████ and if and how I bled.

Age ████████ a very bad ██████████████████. I knew and I didn't ████. You ruin ██████████ and nothing after matters. So I kept ██████. Because of ██████, I cannot trust ██████████ I cannot be in ████████████ a man ████████████ I cannot be in ██ ████████ with my body ████████████.

Every ████ tried ████████ suicide and ███.

Age ████████ and losing ████████████, because I chose ████ over ███.

Every other ██████████ ruined because I couldn't █████████████████ to love me.

*

After the procedure, I remained still in that room for what felt like fourteen days or at least several hours. But there was no clock and what does it matter anyway. I heard a knock and Marlory walked in. She smiled, but without teeth and I worried something went wrong. So much is revealed in a closed-mouth smile.

"███████, █████ well. Here, in the south ████ people ████████████████████ become like ████████████ floating away from ███████████ are, I took parts of ██ ████████ like quicksand. Your ████████ had stranded you. Now, you can █ on. Now you can l██ without ████████ calendars behind ██. Now, you can █ free."

I took a deep breath. My throat felt scratched, scratchy, like someone had raked my insides, gathered up my guts like a pile of leaves.

"I feel," I said, "████ like █████ I can █████████ despite...█████...wait...I can't ██████ ████████ █████████ █████, cannot remember why ███████. I feel...I feel... possible."

JOHN J. TRAUSE

Scandinavian Dilemma

What to do this morning?   So many choices:

Make breakfast   Walk the dog   Get drunk (no, I am already drunk)

Have sex   Visit mother in the nursing home   Have an abortion

Text a friend   Commit suicide   Pack lunches for Karin and Gunnar

Finish reading the novel   Stare at the playground for three hours

File for a divorce   Go skiing   Smile   Tell Halvar that I may love him

Strip the house of any sentimental remnants   Let the spider out of the house

Leave for Tjörn   Stay in bed all day   Fake a smile   Go to work

Do the laundry   Drive to the country   Pick cloudberries   Watch TV

Cut myself with glass   Buy a new dress   Telephone Ingrid

Listen to the radio   Become a lesbian   Go to the gym   Cry

Rearrange the cabinets   Remember having a feeling   Open the windows

Induce vomiting   Go to the market   Make coffee   Go to the movies

NEELI CHERKOVSKI

I Love Dead Poems

Especially when they destroy
My sleep and force men
Into the garden, I love dead
Poems that talk about
Themselves, I love the death
Of poetry, what is better
Than the dead trees and the
Clouds moving across the
Rocky Mountains? Does anyone
Doubt the momentary?
Life comes and goes, death sticks
Around for billions of years

My neighbor came for coffee
And we sat in a blizzard talking
About dead poets, not those
Ancient Greek and Chinese
But those covered in deer skin
During the Ice Age or down
In a silent world of wood and
Grass, I like to think of them
I said because they dreamed of me
And of our grief and tragedy

DANIEL ARISTI

Whippomorpha

Rescued dolphin tangled in fishing net. And my first reaction
Is oh to find him a job—
It's the way they denounce without saying,
Their blowhole like a gunshot wound like, "Hey
I'm still Lazarus alive," and the non-voice comes from the blowhole
That refuses to heal.

Dolphin's a vet. Navy trains them to kill frogmen
(Sharks can't be trained).
I wanted my dolphin to be good. A chaplain.
Just my luck.
Or a medic.

Dolphin's killing me.
Who's counting but? (It's almost pleasurable). Last
I peeked into the lesion—as if His side wound—
The dark red hydromachine within
Spoke life.

VALERY OISTEANU

Fado Dada

Alfama, Alfama the very narrow streets of Lisbon
Where tiled dreams are sprayed with glue
Where birds with cork beaks fight for ledges
Where ghosts are deep fried and sold to tourists
There the sun shines only for half a minute
By night wounded cobblestones cry under the feet of Fado singers
Broken dreams of a homeless woman with Mozambique eyes
Stay calm and enjoy the cork, everything is made of cork
Even Marilyn Monroe is a pocketbook of cork
Black student robes fly off the clotheslines
Alfama center of reverse gravity, of surreal graffiti
The Monastery looms large and chimes incessantly
The Queen and King of Portugal enjoy a noisy afternoon
Tuk-tuk drivers equipped with abrasive shouts
Smashing the tower of Belem-Babel cacophony
Pessoa's absinthe not sold here, muscatel, gingia & Porto
Two fat chefs cook pork fat and chicken gizzards
Paving a path to Multiple Personality Disorder
Alvaro de Campos' blessings, Ricardo de Reis disquietude
The road to Coimbra is paved with jagged lives
I regress slowly into Pessoa smoking a long pipe
Words flow, a spell to enter seven gates of Fado-dada

Yes,
the jaws
are exactly as
strong as you
imagine. Some
days stronger.

When   my mother lowers   into
the   pit, the muck bellies   up
to   her chin. She sinks   in,
unable to stay on the shore
and watch the toothy
beasts rise up to her.

Her body waits in its
darkness for the other
darkness to overtake
her. When she feels
their scutes rasp her
toes, she gathers breath in.

My   mother disappears
into the swamp, and we
can do nothing to bring
her back to us. We know
she is rolling with the
monster. We watch how

the bubbles   roil.
She must reel
with the gator
on her own,
though we
stand ready

to reach in.
My mother's
hands on
the snout—
the deadly
spin.

BRITTNEY CORRIGAN

Alligator Wrestler's Daughter

MERRIDAWN DUCKLER

Hippie Women Dancing, Street Fair, Camano Island

(how did I get this old)

Jerk step in rotation with hand flail

(once they couldn't take their eyes off me)

one hand clapping, flapping like a tilted penguin

(eyes took notes)

third hand giving a very lackluster hand-job.

(the bass walking, the trembling fret; the keyboard run up and down,

looking for an opening, little hi-hat clapping out directions to the unlocked room)

Don't stop

(now my torso west and my neck is in the east)

dudes on stage even older.

(my skin is like rubber)

The night split into guitars on the dirty festival floor

(how did my center of gravity get here?)

Open-eyed, my rival is dancing beside me.

(shit)

Old stick, at least I still have shape to shake.

(never stop)

When I wink twice, let's blow their collective minds.

ALEXIS RHONE FANCHER

Ernest, as in Hemingway

(After a Hot Girls' Night at Farfalla on La Brea, We Smoke a Blunt in Lynne's Lexus)

Three hundred days since I'd had sex. The attractive pawnbroker behind the counter who flirted with me had no idea, when he passed me the expensive watch, that the graze of his hand set off sparks. The Cartier was an aphrodisiac; that watch had weight. Its 14K gold and stainless steel band begged to wrap itself around my wrist. I twisted my arm so the Cartier caught the pawnshop's florescent light. Two grand cash was burning a hole in my wallet. I'd hoped it was enough.

There's a tap on the window. Lynne starts the engine. Sue's shotgun, me and Nanette in back. I stub out the joint, reluctantly roll down the window, but dude's not a cop. Late thirties, bearded, skinny white guy. Jewish, given the neighborhood. No threat. He's followed us from the bar, wants to join us, get high, so I open the door, scooch over.

He takes my hand, solemnly introduces himself to each of us. "Ernest," he says. "As in Hemingway."

"I'm a big fan of *A Farewell to Arms*," Sue jokes when he won't let go of her hand. Nanette, who bats for the other team, plays Solitaire on her phone. Our benevolent hostess breaks out another blunt. Ernest settles in, takes a hit, then another. He's rubbing against me, but not in a bad way. Says he owns a pawn shop in Hollywood. I'm in the market for a Cartier Panther. "I have one in stock," he exhales.

Next day, flirting over the pawn shop counter after the "killer deal" he's made me on the watch, an invitation. He'll make me dinner at his place. I think we have a connection. I watch Ernest tackle the coq au vin, hang on his words. He tells me I'm beautiful. We drink too much wine. Then he gives me the tour; says he's cherry-picked all the best pieces from the pawn shop for himself. A Chagall, an Eames chair and matching ottoman grace the living room. "Astonishing," Ernest says, "what folks will part with when they're desperate."

He lights the crystal chandelier over the mahogany dining table, tells me it's "Czech, prewar." He has good taste. Does *he* taste good? That's the liquor and the deprivation talking, and the Thai stick we're smoking adds to my confusion. When he kisses me I kiss him back, allow his hands to roam. Ernest unzips my jeans, reaches inside. I cum when he touches me. Love-starved.

I picture waking each morning in Ernest's white, Spanish stucco bedroom with exposed beams. I could be happy here, lucky at last! Ernest has a house, a good career, not the usual waiter/actor I'm used to bedding, back when I still believed in love. But last night, of the four women getting high in Lynne's Lexus, Ernest had chosen me. Maybe it was about more than the Cartier.

Above the headboard, an obscenely large Miró. An antique beveled mirror reflects us on the bed, and we look wanton, content. On the nightstand, sadly, Ayn Rand. But no one's perfect. I unbuckle his belt, unzip him. Fellate his small, hard cock, wonder how it will feel inside me. When he comes, Ernest does not return the favor. Instead, he zips up my jeans, walks me out.

"Enjoy the Cartier," he says as he finesses me into the car, shuts the door. When I lower the window to say goodnight, he leans in, like he's going to kiss me, ask me out again. Instead, he grips my wrist. Squeezes earnestly. "Can you text me the numbers of your three friends from last night?" he asks. "That was so hot, getting loaded in the car!" He laughs. "Help me out here," Ernest says. "I wanna do you all."

MATTHEW HUPERT

Everday's a Zatoichi Day

You have to be a bit of an undertaker
Have to massage death
or you won't get everywhere

If you can't say
"Man, i almost died"
Keep going
      Keep living
Further   Out

to hone sharp   katana the bullshit back
& come around from the other end

pruning your universe for clarity

Fearless   a sculptor cuts away the marble
where it doesn't look like the horse
Close   Apple peel thin
trimmed tight like the skin of the atmosphere
or the first finger pass pressure
that raises the hairs
unexpectedly

GUY BIEDERMAN

Headlong

It was not sustainable. As if life itself had no shelf life. You knew it could only end up a train wreck even when the tracks were clear and countryside rolled by. The porter was tipped and dismissed, his services not needed. The sleeping car had everything—stocked mini fridge, mini bottles of Johnny Black, picture window, fold out bed, eye shades, ear muffs, pillow mints, and Alexa, who was fluent in Thelonius and Trane. Three rolling days stretched endlessly ahead with a Pirate Poet in the dining car, the stately women who silently said grace, a card trickster, and Stingy Brim Brother with an unlit pipe. Rolling away from the past, you knew it couldn't last; a life in robes, love in the afternoon; aware the moment would become memory, the way people become photos and objects they leave behind—denim shirt, belt buckle, felt hat, photograph, a laugh, a final cigarette before dawn in a no-smoking car with windows open, moonlit triangle on the floor, towel tucked under the door as if no one would know. No one but you. Until it was only you. And the train. And the wall. Headlong.

JOSE OSEGUERA

Gotas de Sangre

Blood Drops

When you're little,
You only hear things
Not knowing what they mean,
As when grampa stared at the red
Dripping with bloodshot eyes,
Their sting snapping behind my ears.

Work, work, work
And work was all he knew—
It was his music—
And when he wasn't working
He was working on getting more work.

The few times I ever saw him off his feet
Were in his garden, watching the plants
As they grew the way they grew;
Making sure we didn't rip
The flowers off the pomegranate,

And write our names
In long distorted striplings
On the stucco's bumpy white,
Under the window where grandma
Scolded the cranky wives of La Sánchez Taboada:
Ain't nobody gonna love my kids
The way he loves them.

He placed a hand on his waist,
And reached out to a tree with the other.
He stripped one of its many arms;
The sapling bled sap:

I hit you so that it hurts and you learn,
Because those motherfuckers out there,
Won't hurt you;
They'll kill you.

Although he wasn't my father,
Or my father's father,
That day, his grace
Broke the skin,
Bleeding through shirts for a week.
I hated him for teaching me
The only way he could,

Because he talked the way he was:
Straightforward and simple-hearted.
Most times, he didn't say anything—
Listening to sad songs to cheer himself up
As he drank a concoction of cinnamon tea,
Beer, and sugarcane liquor—
But when he did, he'd do it.

Even after he lacked the strength
To speak, or breathe—
When his eyes were taped shut
Because they wouldn't close—
Before he died,
His veiny hands
Rolled off the hospital sheets
As cracked pomegranates—

Beautiful, purple, delivered—
Open for birds to eat out of:
They could no longer show me
Right from wrong,
As the strongest man I knew
Was finally at rest.

The gashes he branded me with
Grew branches and leaves
That healed beyond my body
Always seeking the light;
A truth that scarred the child
So that the person
Emerging from its husks
Could grow to be complete.

The bittersweetness in every drop
Of pomegranate blood
Lingered in the aftertaste
Of all the things
He never got to teach me.

JARED SMITH

What Fingers on These Keys

I'm sorry. The fingers on these keys
are not my own. The walls are white
the way you like them the day dawning,
and there is a purpose in this outside us

       behind the walls white with peace
       built in mechanical infrastructure
       with microphones and cameras

as you undress the woman you have met
who is beyond anything you can imagine
the two of you are tabulated. You know
nothing of this, but your whale song voices
the scent of your passion your warmth
skin against skin and eyes deep into eyes
as unique as the cosmos you are born into
is here in this room categorized and filmed.

       I'm sorry. This was not my computer
       but one I bought from an online store,
       and I do not know the workings of it—
       who placed what chip upon what chip
       anymore than I know the programmer.

But it is in a white room with an ocean view
where you can watch the shrimp boats floating
on the sea just beyond your reach netting in
morsels that fly from breathing to your plate
beneath a stone moon as soft as memories get

        tabulated from an iron disk
        into a cloud that lasts forever
        that only a computer can read
        and your body fluids are what they are
        as long as you are in the white room
                before frozen

When you are caught thus, no one but the cloud
will remember you and your love is less than stone
and lasts a long, long time which has no meaning.

JANET HAMILL

Bearing Witness

When my brother came back from the volcano
we walked together past streams of lava—
two grotesques in overcoats.

I took him to Café Vallejo.
High in the Andes
beneath a photograph of *Los Heraldos Negros*
a cold glass of lemonade
came to boil in his throat.

I looked at him—
all red like me.

He spoke of bearing witness
inside the volcano—
his lips were cracked & swollen.
his hands badly burned—
held to a flame by maenads,
at the bottom.

I looked at him—all red like me.

He cried—
Tear out my eyes spilling over with hot rain!
Tear out my eyes. Tear them out! Please, tear them out!

ADINA DABIJA

Ahah-sahah-ala!

ah my dear
you make me say: ahah-shahah-ala!

Nothing else that I could say would be

Ahah-shahah-ala – I yelled
one August evening on my porch
the day I first opened that green
book of yours from Penguin
and I heard the wind whispering through your words
dancing out of the page
like leaves
on some big tree

ah my dear
how you flow through days and nights
filling everything that has no name, just
– ahah-shahah-ala! –
echoing between the curved surfaces of your soul
for the spirit to play
hide and seek in between
words
that are not yours
because it is your very nature
for you not to be you
but me

You!...
You are the whistle blown by the breath
of what it is
now
moving through space and time
stirring
this sparkling dust
dancing in the twilight

I knew you
even before I held you on my knees
on my porch, that evening in August

some say you are a poet
from 14th century Persia
your books are on the highest shelves
of the greatest libraries of the world
but Hafiz! what you really are
is
ahah-shahah-ala!

ANTHONY MORALES

Sword Split

When kingsblood café noir caravele single late tulips waterfall petals on tops of hairy chest, that's when you know the lord been with you since since. Nothing ever done been bad, if able to scoop up this muse in time to save own life. Before you spark that, walk around, examine surrounding, everyone else searching, but there you sit, rewriting deadly derivative of lonely algorithm. Functional futuristic litness, unfortunate frazzle, considerable spazzle, shoulders shriek stress. Best of skinny me, lift head & see, more than L O W. Els from O left a dub or two. Back with nothing left, holla at local benevolent. Blessed recognition, if scratch still switch. When is the transition, perfect temperature, heights of horizon despite clouds thriving parching soil, wrinkling skin, rough palms, side by glide. Hug me back, kiss me first, you on top, take me there. Now we here, smile so bright, why heart dark. Hold us close. Please don't leave. All about, once often, then never. But how do we still reach, meet me someday. Be waiting on notice, sin falta, te lo juro, I swear. No one else sight from distance, finally paid attention so could ask question out loud. So special, one of you, el todopoderoso de crowd. Ponte a llorar, sit & pose for pretty picture, laugh wild.

2003

Haribo Gummi Bears have pig bones in them. They do. Haribo Gummi Bears contain gelatin, which is crushed pig. People are grossed out by that, but they eat ham and pork and bacon. It's the meat we're okay with.

I'd always bite the head off first. That's just how you eat gummy bears. In eighth grade, we stuck them together, bear-dick to bear-gina, and made kissy noises, made moans we didn't understand yet. On the band bus, we'd stick their flat backs against windows and made bets on whose would stay the longest, on the strongest bear.

Our bus driver was Mrs. Dookie. I'm not kidding. She was old and droopy, and wore purple eyeshadow. She was mean—that's that. Mrs. Dookie was always yelling, and her voice shook when she did it. She would yell, and we would mimic her yell back, exaggerating the shake, like something big caught sideways in a yawning throat. Mrs. Dookie didn't have a husband, but her name was Mrs., so maybe she did once.

"Mrs. Poopie," we would yell, and we would shake.

Haribo Gummi Bears are boiled bones, skin, and tendons. A pig's foot has sixteen bones in it, and they are very small. Skittles also have pig bones in them. Marshmallows have a lot of pig bones. But they, the pigs, have the most pig bones. Pigs have the most pig bones until a little kid, sixty pounds, eats his weight in gummy bears; maybe he's got more pig bones than a pig's got pig bones.

Pigs can digest human bones. Two Detroit-area hunters went missing in 1985, and their bodies were never found. In 2003, brothers Raymond and Donald Duvall were sentenced to life without parole. They had bludgeoned the two hunters to death and fed their bodies to pigs. The pigs left nothing behind.

I don't know the guys' names, the ones that got fed to pigs. But the guys in prison—they're the Duvall brothers. And I remember being a kid, screaming and laughing, and gummy bear climaxes. And I remember Dookie, but not who loved her enough to make her a Mrs.

DANIEL DISSINGER

concerning a...

I want to show them each crooked neck
and silver set of hands

nakedness is not undressing
but to release this pressure

from you(r)

veins and arteries
all over the sidewalk   to(o)

tell stories about each drop of paint
as it hardens   can it release nothing more than everything
of yourself across these windows   and drown you(r) feet
and hands   wash you(r)   chest and belly with whatever
life might be left

make sure you've fallen asleep
and then
I can perish   naked—
                         ness   ...I want them to know
beyond   flesh beyond genitals beyond   perfection   ...I
can reach inside myself and tear my heart through this
breastbone   plant your tulips there   in it   I might die
with that taste of sunlight shattered over my lips

and because my body is her body   when his body greys
and because my body   ...I will only be winter
like photographs of your dragged moonlight diminished
on that lake...

ELLEN POBER RITTBERG

What I think about when I think in my morning commute, and you complicit

When we fight sleep do we fight death
The
The un-aspired to
The thing in the closet
That may be alive
That isn't meant

And we know it
On some level we know it
The dust ball
From disused sweater
A tatter of plastic seen
Seemingly teeming
organic
Comedic almost antic,
That   that great fooler
Adrenalin thumper
The choice prime steak
Runny pink
I never eat but once did
Okay maybe thrice
Don't think of that either
Not because of any
widely held beliefs
The broad berth
Of my beliefs astonish
But just

Chewing I find arduous
Don't know why
My teeth are strong
Yellow-ish like a horse
Is she kidding
No
That was how

They judged health
in days of then or
Yore
Let us say yore
Yes let's
Great word
Got to get
Got to get the word in play
Acquisitive-like
Got to be in it
To win it
Thus spaked the New York
Lotter-ay
Aye as affirmation
What happened to that?

May I bray
I have the teeth for it
May I construct as Tinker Toy construction
As well constructed grammatical function
As in you will you say yes, yes
Don't ask
Shall we
Politesse
Do I belong here
In this here-here

In this eon
Mesozoic
Paleotropic
Never can keep them in order
Not that it matters
Still there's a
Critical mass

DEBORAH KENNEDY

Habeas Corpus

I. In Runnymede's muddy meadow, the glorious proposition arises
    A. The Great Charter of Liberty is carefully inscribed on sheepskin parchment
        1. When it's held aloft, people cheer loudly and wave their arms
        2. Some still grip the hilt of their swords
    B. Six hundred years later, the glorious proposition is our bedrock
        1. Unfortunately, we never notice the ground until there is an earthquake

II. Remembering things is a lot of work
    A. Long ago, we believed that God appointed kings
        1. Kings believed they should hire men to wipe their asses
        2. You wipe your own ass
    B. Today, the King has not mounted your head on a pike at the city gates
        1. Or even the head of someone you might like to see there
        2. No one notices

III. Teachers stop speaking of the glorious proposition
    A. Everyone forgets almost everything
        1. Anyhow, who knows Latin anymore?
    B. History is just a lot of stuff that already happened
        1. Is the Suspension Clause suspended?
        2. This all happened a long time ago, right?

IV. Change is expectable but by its very nature, unpredictable
    A. Something happens
        1. It is not called by its true name
        2. This works as well as it ever did
    B. They call them "rendered persons"
        1. This does not refer to lard

V. Thinking is also a lot of work
    A. Today, we celebrate forgetting everything we have forgotten
        1. This apparently includes what happened yesterday
        2. Will the sun ever set on the second most Patriot Act?
    B. No one wakes up in the morning and says, "Hey, they could render me next."
        1. Equality before the law can cut two ways
        2. Besides, exactly what is lard and how is it rendered?

VI. We all walk on the edge of a knife
    A. It hurts
        1. We ignore the pain
    B. Which way will we fall?
        1. Falling usually doesn't kill you
        2. Landing can
        3. Who will have the bodies then?

FRANCES OGAMBA

The Grandpa Whose Head Was Not Correct

The grandpa dozed on the Adirondack chair. His teenage grandson walked past him and disappeared into the house while he snored lightly. A force flipped him into the sky and he spiraled and landed outside the gate. The sun was either amber or gold, both were colors of freedom. The sand had lost some of its brownness, its gritty teeth shone orange. The grandpa moved away from the gate, nobody ever lets him leave. They treated him like his head was empty. His grandson always said, *Lock the gates always. Grandpa may go missing.* Yet right now, as he sauntered down the street, he knew his way. He knew the shoe factory. Ghosts of slaughtered cows and goats floated into view, like flags. They covered the skies. They were the horizon. They were as many as all the leather shoes the factory had ever turned out. The grandpa was barefooted, no shoes to lose to the angry ghosts.

He saw some cows and children coming his way. The children were like the cows and the cows were like the children. There was a bit of a river nestled down the road. The cow children and the children cows walked into it. The water was shallow and murky with animal dung. He was hopeful to get water from another source, a nearby spring maybe. Two dogs walked up to him, friendly at first, and then they barked. The dogs had human faces. The dogs were people he knew. The dogs were his wife who was probably in the bathroom when he left, and his grandson who was probably on his phone right now swiping his right forefinger across the screen.

Right after the dogs came two goats. The animals came in even numbers, and in the smallest even number, two, a number that splinters all the even numbers in existence, even in their trillions. The goats wore the faces of his two sons. One of the goats barricaded his way, and the other, the older of the two charged at him with his horns. It went up on hind legs and came down with the forelegs hard. It repeated this twice as hard. When they grew tired, they left his way and went to the bush nearby to chew fodder. Their jaws worked in a way that was beautiful, that made the grandpa want to grab some of the fresh grass and chew along.

There was emptiness in the wind as he wound down the path, deeper and farther, until he reached the church. He hadn't been there in a decade; he had forgotten the bland taste of wafers, the bite of the alcohol, which doubled as the blood of Jesus, down his throat. A serene wind wafted across the low brick fence to his side of the road. He toyed with going in or moving on. Fresh memories of his wife on their wedding day flared up in his mind. How many lifetimes ago had that been?

The universe thrived with the theory of loss or without.

You lose time or you are without time.

You lose your youth and you are without your youth.

You lose wealth or you are without wealth.

You lose your memory and you are without your memory.

As the grandpa thought of these things, he had long moved past the church. The market loomed into view. The mud-walled stores had grown into something different and sturdy. Were those cement walls and corrugated zinc plates? Where had the rafters gone? Time had moved on and everything he knew of his past had been drowned in that particular lake. The market was deserted; vultures hovered by the butchers' shops.

He found a corner and urinated. Then he passed effluent too and wiped his butt with a paper he found floating about.

He was thirsty, so he sought water. He found nothing. His throat was parched, even desert sands paled in comparison. He badly needed a drop of something, any liquid would do. He saw an orange tree by the roadside. It stood alone and unaltered. The wind scattered the fragrance of the fruits and the grandpa inhaled it and walked faster until he reached the tree. The tree grew unfriendly and quickly hid its oranges from view. The grandpa recognized its branch, pale and pocked like an infected tongue. The orange tree was related to the one he once grew in his compound, which was uprooted because he had to create space for his fish pond (though all the fish all died off in the first year). Someone who ate an orange must have loved it and must have taken the seeds and must have planted them by the road. He walked on.

The clouds were the same shade with his pajamas, a dark blue. He had no idea how long he had walked, but it looked like it was going to rain. He was growing tired, but he was elated to use his legs again, after so long a time, after a doctor sick in the head declared him sick in the head, after his family confined him to a chair.

A crowd rose behind him, like birds in their thousands. Like seagulls stirred from their sea rooms. Their smell to him was the smell of seasons, the coming of the rains or the heat. They shuttled and shuttled into view, his grandson and his wife leading the pack. Something frantic and urgent shook the earth and shook him too. The voice of his grandson sailed across distances and reached him.

"Grandpa! Grandpa! Grandpa!"

The crowd was speaking in one voice, his grandson's. His body shook again, more violently. He could not bring himself to go all the way back, and he needed water so badly. He found a gate and walked through.

The voice of the crowd, of his grandson, came again as a distant sea wave. It was the same tone he used when he said, *Grandpa, please don't flush the toilet. You will mess up the whole place.*

Now the voice was worried and panicky.

"Grandma, please come! Grandpa passed urine and feces on his body, and he won't wake up!"

ISA GUZMAN

Titere Ring

Ghosts fit loose on the finger

              holy broken bodies by a solemn fire
     island more than just fragments of memory or imagination

men gather tentatively at the corner

           desolate cuchifritoes of the mind
          speak the eternity beyond you in gauzy sapphires
             speaking of survival & the precious things
                   unkept

purple sunsets along Avenue C   our ancestry
             signified
             impressionistic genocide

    men gather tentatively at the corner   prayers rounded back again
             beads of tears & bacardi
             gathered in red threads

what's true or not isn't important   what is felt

     heart pouched in grey palms for too long
         purpled afternoon bruises
            the time Papi left home
          & came home
             drunk

sun rises and sets still
    sons cross the last green horizons   Men
           drunk

                                                            on sound
                                                            on voices
                                                            on laughter

a chord holds on orange fire pits
                        lined against the skull   meditation worth something

        burnt & balanced on a shadow   bachata   salsa   bolero jazz

the ribcage holds a string of colors one sees by listening
                    old poets find their books in concrete
                                                        a ceaseless playing
                                                        an intersection of mental ends
                                                        a ceaseless search for meaning

Mythology broken more than once

                                    men gather tentatively at the corner

under searchlights & street lights

                                                        without a cycle of birth
                                                                        death
                                                                        after-life

worn sometimes without warning

                                                        we won't want the world to shake
                                                            but to finally come to rest
                                                            papers out of every pocket
                                                            song on every tongue
                                                                    in tongues
holyed   someday
        ourselves into puro breath
                        puro voice
                                puro patria   free
                                                   free
                                                   libre

YUKO OTOMO

a table in the corner

1. petit dejeuner

a woman
with a feather
on her lips
sighs a lovely sigh

a man watching her
sees a shadow
tremble

the voice of the forest
& voices of birds
merge into daybreak
brightly

2. dejeuner

take off your mask
take off your coat
the entrance & the exit
do not always share
both ends of a straight line

who will witness
TIME's impression
as it stops
way above
our heads?

3. diner

when we listen to the ocean
of "PLEASURE TENDENCIES"
laying down on our bellies,
it bounces back at us,
saying
"it is impolite
 to ask me for assurances"

to lose ourselves
in a landscape
for the passion of self-expression
is filled with
a muteness
of falling into the sky

you & I, together,
wonder why
"a heart" seems
so precious

4. dessert

a struggling effort
to pursue
an adventure
to carry
light & shadow
balancing well
in both hands
leaves us
in an overly exotic mood

oh,
we need
something
to wash our numbed tongues

a circle, a whole, a map

no analytical jargon
will ever explain
the need
& its whys & whens
to anyone
in any situation

renegades that we are—
we won't slap
each other's cheeks
for self-liquidating reassurance

rather,

we feed dust
to our favorite pets
when they finish
their big meals

KATHARYN HOWD MACHAN

Krahe

Fox will paint the meadow where
the black crow stalks, winter
silvering tufts of wheat
left behind by careless reapers,
havens for small mice escaping
blade and tooth and beak.

Old Germany, before
Hitler's rise, high
gray boots, gray helmets hard
enough to hold bold thoughts inside
any heads beginning to question
why all Jews must be killed.

Smooth crow with gleaming wings
tight and taut and ready
to fly if threatened. Fox
has read the stories shared by women
collected by the Brothers Grimm.
Old Germany. Before.

DAN RAPHAEL

Rained In

[handwritten inscription: Sorry for the... street..., Brad — signature]

So much rain falling
none of the drops can be connected
as one way as time
crossed by the wind running from—
the pressures always lower on some other side
where people forgot to grow
no stream to follow
the trees swore the birds to secrecy

The street looks like a river
too dazed to flow
my doors not ready to open yet
a change in data
a high probability of the same old shit
odor free ennui

The lone crow cant fly in this rain
looking for an overhang to hop to

Dont know the rains color
til it pools, too glutinous to bow
the street is imagining soup—
salt, fat and simmered roots

If leaves decided to pull in and never let out
seed going the wrong way on a one way
when roots flower, when we gather enough pollen to rail
before the wind clears the stage for more rain

JOAN GELFAND

Migrate

Land crabs crawl, clack-clacking to the sea,

Skitter under night skies

Beneath porches, across driveways, through rose gardens.

Many calcified shells crunch eerily beneath car tires.

Still, they heed the sea's call, the scent.

Katya, trailing blue hijab, ran two years

Afghanistan to Iran. Iran to Greece.

Wires, crossed. Corrupted logic. ISIS.

Separated by a mountain of documents, her mother washes up

In the west, Katya left behind, stuck as a crab in mud.

On the move, migrants scurry from dry hills, drug lords,

Cartels, suicide bombers, heroin.

Tunnel below fences, traveling defenseless.

On Lesvos, Michele is valiant, heeds the call of the sea.

Survival lesson #1: Tread water. Crawl. "This is how you swim."

Her warmth a salve to wounds of lost parents, capsized boats,

Drowned babies. Michele walks on water

A gentle greeter of displaced souls.

FRANCINE WITTE

Daddy sits us all at the table

and tries to tell us about life. He starts with an orange. My mother had put a bunch of them in a bowl, all nice and hilly, before she left us for good. Now they were nothing but brown little stones.

"You see this orange," he says anyway. "It started out juicy and full of hope."

"Excuse me," my soon-dead brother, Billy, says. "How can an orange be filled with hope?" This was a fair question, but I suspect it's the kind that will eventually get him killed.

Daddy shrugs and says, "Okay, let me try this with a fish." So he pulls one out of the cookie jar. We are smacked silly with the stink. It is gouged with rot and we are glad to finally be addressing it.

"Are you going to slice off its belly?" my Aunt Noma wants to know. "I'll gladly eat it with my lunch."

"Can't you see how spoiled it is?" Daddy almost says.

He turns around for a knife and Noma slips it in her purse. "If you give a dead thing purpose," she winks at us, "it's sort of still alive."

When Daddy turns back and sees the fish missing, along with Aunt Noma, he tries another way.

He walks us over to the nursery, the secret room we don't talk about. Where my brother, Baby X, died after only one week.

"This is what you need to know about life." He points to the crib I only saw once, and that was when it was empty. Either before or after Baby X.

Not during. Never during.

Daddy goes on to tell us how life is a garden. You water it. You run a hose. You think of what the seeds will grow into. You try to forget that death is also a seed.

THOM CAGLE

They Smoked Together

He was a Marlboro
light, long, and stretched
out white boy, rolled
up tight, filtered
but strong enough to take a break
and grab a hit
from the lips of some handsome
fellow hazard, a Winston tease
in his thirties, one tall low talker
and smooth—
They were both already raging
before it got started. He flicked away
he dropped to the ground
and they burned down Philadelphia in an hour.

SARAEVE FERMIN

Ode to the Unmade Children

For what is a body if it does not do what it is made for?
Every month my insides turn violent and the moon sends
the promise of what I am built for out to sea.   Oh,
what a home I could have swaddled for you, smothered in
fleece blankets, adorned in naps and greedily stolen
moments of last freedoms, kept complacent with banana
cream pie milkshakes and prenatal vitamins.   Avocados and
kale smoothies, feet propped up, never a stressed heartbeat.
Snuggled away, nine months of small voices and blessed
affirmations.   How the women in my family multiply.   How I
know you would have been a girl.   Girl with high cheekbones
and unflinching jaw.   How I would have born you like a wolf
but raised you like a fox in this world.   How I keep you safe—
a name tucked behind the ear, never to be sacrificed.

SHARMINI WIJEYESEKERA

On the Nature
of Controversy

Start with cunt—
well you've got
one, and no matter how
you try and dress it up
someone, somehow
is gonna point it
out—like it's some
sort of clever gimmick
you've stuck down
between your legs
for the attention.
Might as well beat
them to the punch.

G.G. SILVERMAN

rites for women to perform upon waking

1.

Run your fingers over your skin. Name the hurts, count the scars. Gather the bodies of murdered sisters, heap their bones for reckoning.

2.

Stand naked in a circle of snakes for protection. Close your eyes, breathe deeply, fill your belly with fire. On the dark stage of your mind, concentrate: envision your body's a gun.

3.

Eat the hearts of hunters to know their ways. Guard your daughters with tooth and razor; give them magical names: *Vengeance*, *Maleficum*, *Fearsome*.

4.

Form a small woman of clay. Weave your hair for her clothes, pluck your teeth for her eyes. Scribe the names of bad men on her palms. Whisper the word *kill*, open the door.

5.

In a field far from the city, dig a hole as wide as your hand. Scream in the earth as long as you must, release the seeds of your anger. Water your darlings with tears and blood, moan their songs of sorrow. Watch knives grow tall in the field, see how they glint in the sun. Harvest the daggers, the swords, the scythes. Set some aside for reaping, forge the rest as your throne.

6.

Sever the ear of a rapist; coat it in honey, put it under your tongue. Stand in the subway at midnight, hear men's malevolent thoughts. From a safe distance, snap their necks with a flick of your wrist.

7.

To break the backs of the slavers, weave three men out of straw. Circle them backwards
three times, cleave them in half with an axe.

8.

To prevent the resurrection of the Bluebeards, search for their graves, exhume their remains.
Douse their corpses in oil, burn them to ash. Smash their headstones: erase their names.

9.

File the teeth of boys until they're no longer demonic, feed them rose water and pearls.
Bind their fists in ribbons and lace, and set them loose in the wild.

10.

On a high plain, build a tower of cards with only kings, kings, kings.
Summon the winds, thunder, deluge; topple the kings to the earth.

11.

Chant the bones of your sisters to life.

MIRA MARTIN-PARKER

In the Garden of the Consul General

During the Age of Reason. Or was it Modernity? Or some Post kind of time? They start with the tongue, then move on to other emotions. See something, say something. They can use that one as well. Technology. Each finger, a screen. We are a clean species, so why wouldn't one trust a small removal, a few issues with the face. Bend over, a quick email is sent. Then it's off with both arms, while classical piano plays on. An order, that's nice. Leadership, several billion dollars worth. A deal, in a few quick slices. Trust is good, cooperation. Try this one at home. Nose to tail. A tale, an export, a culture, climate, freedom, fingers first. In the modern era, warfare is a way of life—one life—plus an epidemic, a school bus, and then the check arrives. In an instant, it's a new game. Never mind. This is only a minor complication, a small difficulty. Globalism. Nationalism. Rationalism. Pragmatism. Animalism. *Homo economicus*, the reasonable chooser, the enlightened consumer. Can someone please point me to the checkout line? I'm afraid things haven't worked out so well. Never mind, I'll just stand behind this man. He looks like he's missing.

MICHAEL SUTTON

Bailiwick

This has been the best two months of my year.

Fresh kidneys stuffed
in my garage. I sat up

frightened by reflexive wishes,
more than a teaspoon of blood I spat up,
and twilight was a crippled curtain.
Whichever way you look at it

we are stuck in this centrifuge,
succumbing to divorce, most likely
you go your way

        and I end up in the plaster room,
           minimised and mummified,
               used as a footstool,

scorned for the uneven surface of my back,
           ultimately nugatory footstool feeling

sorry for itself.

I used to have a rabbit stuffed,
        ears black from my nosebleeds,
I cherished and adored her
though her skull was too small for her brain.

PAUL SMITH

Death and Taxes

The reverse mortgage seemed simple. Just fill out some paperwork, send it in, and Roz and I would start getting some money every month instead of sending it in. I filled out everything. Checks arrived monthly in the mail. A burden had been lifted. The two bedroom tri-level we'd lived in for years was paying us back, saying a big 'thank you'. We'd remortgaged several times, constantly putting things off, increasing our payments through job loss, medical problems, depression, substance abuse, counselling. But now we were saved.

Then after four months, a note came in the mail. Two notes.

"You agreed to what?" Rosalyn said.

"I guess I agreed to die next week," I mumbled. "That's what this thing says."

"Let me see that *thing*, as you call it."

I handed the thing to Roz. It had a name. It was called *Agreement of Early Termination of Both Parties, Amendment to Reverse Mortgage/Annuity/Spanish Prisoner Deal*. Rosalyn's eyes scanned the lengthy document, all in fine print. It read 'You have to die next week.'

"That's your signature, alright. The whole thing is fine print. How could you sign a thing like this?"

"I didn't know I was supposed to read the reverse mortgage. I just thought I had to sign it."

"This agreement is in both of our names. It's not just you. Now we both have to die. Rats."

I looked at Rosalyn, then at the inside of the house. Then I thought of Rosalyn's insides, how they must be shaking right now.

"My insides are shaking," she announced. "I think I'm going to throw up."

While Rosalyn started vomiting, I started thinking. There had to be a way out of this. We were supposed to be getting money back for years, I thought for up to thirty years, the length of a standard mortgage. Or until I died. I really should start to read things.

Rosalyn returned from the sink and asked me, "What else does it say?"

"I don't know. It's too long to read. I give up."

"Let me see it," she said. "It says here we can appeal. But we have to do it today. That's what the fine print says. We have to go to the Bureau."

"The Bureau of Federal Investigation?"

"No."

"The Bureau of Internal Revenue?"

"No, the Bureau of Bureaucracy."

That had an ominous sound to it that I didn't like. I repeated it.

"There's an echo in here," Rosalyn said.

I had dealt with bureaucracies before. They were awful. You had to fight fire with fire, though. Earth with earth. Dust with dust. I went upstairs to our strongbox where we kept our papers. They had papers. I had papers. Fight paper with paper, I thought. I felt powerful and invincible. Then I realized Roz and I didn't have a lot of papers. We had a reverse mortgage and a wedding license. That wasn't much to go on, or fight with. I was going to fight anyway. It's not the size of the dog in the fight; it's the size of the fight. This would be a big fight. Roz would see to that.

"What's that other note?" Rosalyn asked.

"It's about our property taxes," I read. "We owe tax money. I thought the reverse mortgage covered that. But we're broke. I was counting on the reverse mortgage."

"Did you read it?"

"Yes," I said. I thought I heard that question before.

Roz looked at me.

"No."

Then Roz and I looked at our house. It wasn't much, but it was all we had—a beige tri-level, half-brick and half siding. It was a hybrid, not quite urban, not really suburban-looking. Inside was more beige paint, furniture that was not extravagant, stuff on the walls from Target. Everything here spoke of compromise, an accommodation Roz and I had made to get by.

We went downtown to the Bureau of Bureaucracy. It was downtown. That's why we went there. I thought we'd see a big monolithic structure that Stalin might have built; faceless and imposing, intimidating to folks like us who didn't have a clue. But it was a tall spire with convoluted balustrades and cornices and things I read about in art class once and forgot. It impressed me with its elegance and pinochle or savoir faire or élan or something else I didn't have a clue about. It looked French. We went inside an enormous lobby, where all the bureaucracies were listed. There was the Bureau of Standards, the Bureau of Death, the Bureau of Taxes, the Bureau of Continents, the Bureau of Incontinence, the Bureau of Incompetence, the Bureau of Contents, the Table of Contents, the Bureau of the Water Table. There were bureaus for everything. And overseeing it all, there was the Bureau of Bureaucracies, which had no office. I liked it here. It felt homey. If Roz and I didn't have a house, I wouldn't mind living here.

We got on the elevator and wound up on the wrong floor. There were miles of cubicles. It was comforting to see all that beige, to see the tops of heads buried in paperwork. It appealed to my inner bean-counter, my inner paper-pusher, to be around all this busy work of made-up nonsense. Why couldn't I have had a career in a cocoon structure like this place where repetition is revered, where there is nobility in sloth? Maybe there was an open cubicle somewhere where Roz and I could hide out. No one would find us. It would be an Octopus's Garden where we could hold our breath until the very end.

"We're on the wrong floor," Rosalyn said. I snapped out of it. "Where were we headed?"

"Since we're supposed to die, we were heading to the Bureau of Death," I said. We took the elevator two more floors up. A bureaucrat there told us since we were not dead yet, we could not come here, but we could come back as soon as we were deceased. He suggested the Bureau of Taxes, which had to be paid. So we went there.

A receptionist took our names and told us to wait until the office closed. I suspected a trick. I asked to see someone now.

"Define 'now'," she said, her eyes narrowing.

"Like right away," I said.

"We can't do that right now or right away. We can't do anything right."

"How about left? Can you do something left?'

She thought a minute. "Yes, we can. If you leave, then you will have left, and yes, we can help you."

"Rosalyn," I said. "We're leaving."

"Goodbye," the receptionist said.

We went out the door and came right back. Correction. We came left back.

"Yes, may I help you?" the receptionist said.

"We left, so now you can help us."

"Alrighty," she said. "Sit right over there."

"You mean *All-lefty. Sit left over there?*"

"You're a clever one. Mr. Wagstaff will be left with you."

"That's all-left with me," I said.

We waited in the reception area, where there were magazines nobody read, music that no one listened to, and picture frames on the wall with nothing in them. This was a well-organized bureaucracy; I had to give them credit. Pretty soon Mr. Wagstaff came in.

"Hello. Your papers are not in order. Goodbye."

"We haven't shown you our papers. You don't know what we're here for."

"That's our standard greeting. May I see those papers in your hand?"

I handed him the reverse mortgage and the wedding license and the two notes we got in the mail.

"Just as I thought. They are not in order. You need to reschedule."

"What's wrong with them?"

"I've never seen anything like them before. This is my first day."

"We have a reverse mortgage that says we have to die next week. That's just plain wrong. I'm looking to you to protect us. Look over these papers and help us. That's your job."

"Hmm," he said. "Let me read this." Mr. Wagstaff started reading and hmm'd some more. "Well, it's all right here. I mean it's all left here," he gave us a wise smile. "You have to pay your taxes first. Then you can die."

"We don't want to die."

"Then pay your taxes."

A light went on in my dim bulb of a head or something. "So if we don't pay our taxes, we don't have to die, left?"

His brow furrowed. "There is a conundrum."

"Hey, our sex life is off limits!"

"A conundrum, an enigma, a problem. You cannot die until you pay your taxes. You have no money to pay them. You have no money because your reverse mortgage is cancelled. It is cancelled because you have agreed to die next week. This is a catch. Did you know there is a Bureau of Catches? I suggest you go to the Bureau of Death. They may issue a

Revocation of Death Certificate, in which case you can be declared living and breathing again. Then pay your taxes and then you can die. Case closed!" he said triumphantly.

I smelled something rotten. There was something fishy about this whole business, an albatross belonging to the Ancient Mariner was hanging around someone's neck, and that neck was mine. Then I realized it wasn't an albatross at all. It was Rosalyn leaning on me, sobbing quietly. She hated paperwork. How was I going to fight fire with fire, paper with paper with Rosalyn hanging on my neck? I took out a Kleenex so she wouldn't get any more snot on my sleeve and thought, 'Why not fight snot with snot and Kleenex with Kleenex?' I realized I just gave her my last Kleenex and had no snot of my own, so I started thinking, real hard this time. What other papers did I have?

"The wedding license!" I exclaimed. "Let's read the wedding license."

Wagstaff and Roz and I read the license together till I found the clause I was looking for. "There it is!" I said. "'Till death do us part.'"

"And?" Wagstaff said.

"The reverse mortgage is made out to us, to Rosalyn and to me. If we part ways, it is no longer valid."

"Only if you're dead!" Wagstaff said. "Got you there, partner."

"But this note says I have agreed to die, which for all intents and purpose means I am dead."

"I said technically, not legally. Or the other way around."

"But if Rosalyn and I separate now, we'll be dead, because of the wording 'Till death do us part', which partly implies that parting is a form of death. Therefore, as dead persons we are not liable, which is different than technical or legal, and as such, as parties of the first part who have parted company, cannot pay taxes. Which also means this document is null and void."

Wagstaff stared at me. Neither one of us had any idea what I just said, but it partly made sense in the Bureau of Bureaucracies, where words are parsed, that is to say, chopped up fine like parsley. "I sort of see your point," he mumbled. "But you are going to give up your wife of so many years just to avoid dying and paying taxes?"

Rosalyn and I looked at each other. "Yes," we gulped.

"And you're going to give up your house as well?"

"Our house?" we exclaimed.

"The fine print says, *If you don't agree to die when we say so you lose the house*. Do you wish to continue?"

"Yes," Rosalyn said. She was the brains in this marriage. Plus she sort of read the whole document. I didn't. "We want to die when we say so, not when you say so."

"Then," Wagstaff said, "What God has put together, let no man put asunder. Let no man put us under, or something. Did you bring God here as a witness? No? Good. Wait a minute. I'm going to put asunder your marriage. I'm not God. I'm just a piece of snot with a cubicle. Yes, I am God. Or a witness. Who am I? I just started here. Anyway, as soon as you two are separated, I will void this document."

We knew exactly what to do. Rosalyn and I stated emphatically, "We're leaving," and then walked out the door. We had left. Then we came back in separately to have Wagstaff null and void the document.

"I declare everything vull and noid," he proclaimed.

"You mean noid and vull, left?"

"Fully noid and fully vull."

A pass looked between us. That is to say, a look passed between us.

"Null and void," I said.

"Congratulations," he said blithely. "I had no idea this job would be so simple."

Rosalyn and I walked out of the Bureau of Bureaucracies no longer man and woman but simply as Rosalyn and Paul, no longer indentured servants, serfs, Freemasons or Merchant Seamen, just two folks who had beat the Bureau of Bureaucracies at its own game. We walked out into the fresh, French downtown air looking for croissants and realized we now had no place to live.

I stared up at the Bureau of Bureaucracies gleaming spire and said, "Laissez les bons temps rouler!"

"Wow!" Rosalyn said. "I didn't know you spoke French. What does that mean?"

I looked up again at the tower holding the Bureau of Bureaucracies. Maybe somewhere near the Bureau of Catches there were two empty cubicles, one for me and one for Roz. A lump formed in my throat as I proclaimed:

"There's no place like home."

ERIK RICHMOND

The Opera Singer's Wife

One of these days
she will walk through her living room
naked as Venus on the half-shell
forgetting or simply not giving a damn
that the lights are on and the blinds up
and the lonely old man next door
glancing up from his morning coffee
at exactly the right moment
will hear a chorus of angels
singing more sweetly
than her husband ever did

STEVE DALACHINSKY

The Outhouse

in the back of the barn
late 1830's
outhouse   apart
falling in on itself
below there some feet
the pile of excrement
ours   theirs   & the   baby's

good   morrow   to you morning coffee   premature
  awakening
            my tomatoes won't make it with this weather
      squooshy if they do
                    bingo - get that cow offa my psyche   fellers
        wind says   pushing the big clouds toward town
                working the leaves   like field hands

embracement
behavior
organizational
extinguish

                        in the back   late
                      outhouse   1800's
            sits itself
                in half   evenness
          pale shades   of   family & friends
            participating   in   necessities

110

clean slate   em bar(e) ass   me(a)nt   retire   *managerial*   **erase**   electric

a blast of sun
little   fault   my face   content
in   the 1800's   privitization   late in the back in

the   *outhouse.*

CRAIG KITE

Brutalism

The tower has a spirit
because all stones do.
It starspangles the narrative vines
and culture-wars the house ghosts.
And the lack of lobby plants
grows like imaginary spindles.

I know the name
of the man with a lion mane
who lives on the billionth floor.
He calls me him.
He Stuyvesant.
We make like blood and run.

Concrete is a good sounding board
for most men conjuring ambitions at dawn.
I dream about the contours of a saxophone
and blow up lion man.

Stuyvesant has elephant ears,
a golden shower basin,
kitchens of caged finches for breakfast
and exes in his pupils.
He whispers commercial incantations
overtop my tap water
and tells me that my living situation
is small potatoes.

PTR KOZLOWSKI

The flesh against the steel

No, Father wasn't there at the time. He stood at home before the mirror
with the sparkling edge of stainless making scraping noises
up his neck, along his chin line, the same time
sterile gleaming forceps wrapped around your head
to pull you out from Mother, and into touch with instruments.
Not only cutting off your ancestral root, and placing on you instead a clamp,
it wasn't long before they warned your budding stem,
and they made sure your seeds of future life
lost the starting jump out of your gate to blood.
You lay there squirming, waking up in bandage.
Open your new eyes to see your flesh against the steel.

Invent the wheel. Discover speeding past your neighbors.
Discover crashing.
Your shaking lips and frightened tongue detect the
rubbery shards of shredded knee skin broken loose
or still alive somewhere in the taste of muddied blood.
And now the sight impresses: some few feet away, the metal.
It's the eyes that taste the metal thing's rebellion,
the assertion of its logic, the enforcement of this memory
of the flesh against the steel.

Later it's the sounds attacking. Grunts of stamping,
shrieks of tooling, dieing, iron quakes up from foundations,
thuds against the chest and shouts: demands,
metallic as the foundry, for production stepped up,
stepping on who knows whose legs,

to punctuate the minting process puncturing an eye;
the wail of loss at mangled fingers drowned in din but heard as loud
and flavored just as steely
as the clanking, locked-up chains and gates.
And as surely as the axes slowing down the fenders trying to ford the picket lines,
it spells a destiny of handcuffs and the click of rifle hammers.
Hear the grind of armored carriers
now come to press the point
about the flesh against the steel.

It even has its devotees, this flesh against the steel interplay.
Cornering their blood pressure—bottled up inside one limb
to make the vein reach out and touch the chrome alloy.
To touch the shiny tiny pricker point,
and its scent of death, and its closed eyes taste of
cheeks ballooning out in puckers through the chain link and the chicken wire,
the sensation of the wiggling crowd,
who push until they bulge
against the drop-forged,
case-hardened,
tempered,
honed and polished edge
of the known world,
of the envelope of life,
of the what there is.

PJ JONES

The Bath

He likes me this way. I have to do this, if I don't he will know. Rector always knows. I shortcut once with a sink wash, my foot on the edge of the toilet. He refused me, turned away and left. At times I want to say, your nerve, you're not exactly available. But I don't. I won't.

The water is cooling. I'm not much longer in this tub before my skin starts pruning. To think he had this doorway built right after I gave him a key. It was like he had carpenters and plasterers from the 1930s hiding in the closet, waiting for the go ahead. The beautiful Art Deco design precisely drawn with India ink lines on the just baby pink walls around the frame. The men were artisans, craftsmen, I hardly know the difference but they were no band of do-it-yourselfers. Nothing disposable about them. My god, the tieback draping is hung in even pleats and folds. The muted gray feather design on the fabric so striking. The way the plush material pools on the floor on the left side is rich. It gives the bathroom a performance stage entrance. I love looking up at the semicircular valance where the broken transom window above the door used to be. The men were quiet, fast, a vapor of presence, then they were gone. Gone forever and my bathroom transformed in time. Not one took a picture, it was all tucked away in their minds. No memory of the patched rent controlled apartment bathroom could be pulled up. I couldn't recall its existence before. Luxury came to my space; the kind of elegance I've never seen aside from period photographs. One day maybe I will.

Rector is steady. Although his age races ahead of him, he's not elderly. Goodness no, I never speak of him as a senior. His class is frozen in time. He told me he chose me because I seem most affable for his self-illusion. I didn't understand when he said this but the meaning is slowly creeping in.

Is that his key? I have to lift my syrup brown leg as he calls it, and sponge all the way up slowly in rhythm with his steps. It has to be picturesque. I wish he didn't walk so hard. Mrs. Cadwallader, with her dog hearing will be up in a flash complaining, spoiling our time together. She even grumbles when I breathe: it's too noisy, she says. Rector wants her removed from the premises, crazy old bat.

"Rector, is that you?"

"Yes, my beloved, have you deposited a key with another?" His laughter, motion picture resonant, clear and tart.

"I see you are ready for me."

He's always dap. His suit is my favorite, navy blue with charcoal chalk stripes. He knows I love it on him. It makes our time together vagary. I pin my dark coarse hair up just the way he likes it with a cluster of curls on top. I swear he counts them.

"I'm here Rector, right here."

"Coming, my cherished."

His shoulders fill the doorway. His eyes trace my suspended leg to the surface of the milky water preventing him from seeing more of me. That's the way he likes it, hidden so he can say, as he always does, "My heart stops beating when I imagine you." I love when he says that. He has never asked more of me than to just listen to his words. He postures for a moment with his hands aligned evenly on both sides of the doorjamb, hat tilted just enough to expose his grayish temple. I love watching him.

In a breath, he is gone.

I rise out of the bathwater in a bandeau swimsuit. It's Tuesday, this brief time is all he wants until Saturday, when we will go out together to exclusive places to upset the balance, he insists. Where we will be seen and stingingly talked about. Then we'll laugh all the way back to the apartment.

The custom-designed envelope is on the living room end table. The pledge always a mystery yet the surety of never less than five hundred dollars.

CHRISTIAN GEORGESCU

The Corsette

Step right up into my walk-in closet
a walk of shame closet
a walk in secrettes and regrettes
every step of the way in pain closet
we pay against the pain
praying to find out what causes it
hope no one notices
we know what causes it
just hope no one calls us on it
pauses at what causes it
because of it pauses too long
passes on us because of course
This is just the course of things
of course it is
entirely possible this façade
is plausible
hope no one notices
this loneliness
this isolation
is no way of life
for a soul's sojourn
through the world
So please just don't say it
pls just don't spray it
pls don't naysay it
pls let's just say it
once then let's not
and say we did
They say it's a condition
of a dark night of the soul so
Whatever you do
do not call it a master closet
As I have not yet mastered
the closest of pains
the coarsest of pains
this corset of pain laced
tight
tight
tight
with longing
separation

DENISE TOLAN

A Very Short History of Abuse

Lucky Star

I was the only one my father never hit.

I asked my mother why.

You were born under a lucky star, she said.

Is that all I get from the star? I wondered.

My sister couldn't help me with this puzzle because like a modern-day Jack and the beanstalk, she traded all her memories for drugs.

When I turned to my brother, he put his hand over the past as if it was a box of popcorn he would not share.

Why bring up the bad stuff? he said. *Why not think of the vacations we took instead? We had some fun then.*

He speaks something like the truth.

One afternoon, I sat with my mother among a display of lawn furniture at a local garden shop. It was hot outside and we were happy to find comfort beneath the shade of an umbrella marked down to $69.99.

She was eighty-one years old.

Do you hear the birds, Mom?

She cocked her head. *No, my hearing for that is gone.*

Her voice sounded sad. Then she perked up.

But I remember how they sounded: Do do dee dee dee.

I laughed. She laughed. People walking by sent smiles like cool cocktails to the table marked $179.99.

It's so beautiful here, my mother said, as if we were at a resort.

We are the only ones who remember, she said, looking to the horizon at an imaginary sea. *You and me. We remember it all.*

I took her hand. She squeezed mine hard.

I'm sorry, she said. *They are all yours now.*

She would not live another five months.

She was right. I do remember. I remember every scream every plea every sound that pounded flesh can make. And even though nothing landed my way, I hold it all.

Alone now.

Lucky me.

Filament Fail

By the time my mother turned sixty, she was deaf in one ear and mostly there in the other. Every few years we made the pilgrimage for new, miraculous hearing aids. As she grew older, the trips became more like rites of passage.

In the waiting room of the clinic, she tells me: *I don't know if this is anything, but he hit me once, hard on the back of my head, and my ears rang. Then poof—gone. I couldn't hear out of this ear.* She points to the left side of her head.

The doctor calls us in and we go silent.

In the car, I ask why she never told a doctor about being hit.

What could they do?

I nod.

A few days after the left ear, the right one rang, but a little less.

I put on my seat belt and wonder why her ears went out separately, like light bulbs in two different lamps.

I consider the hits to her head. Even if her deafness wasn't his fault, it easily could have been.

Somehow, it's the possibility that burns.

Fast Flash Back

My brother and I slept on our stomachs so we wouldn't see it coming.

Our dad.

His gun.

What did we know?

That he loved us, but hated her enough to do it.
That he was a magician who could wound without ever touching.
My brother and me
Never talk about the fear.

He is a police officer now with his own gun.
I never turn my back.
We are tornado sirens in separate towns.

I'm not sure how my brother sleeps these days.

Someone Else's Past

Everyone has something, my mother would say after my father tore the house apart yet again. *Some men drink, some men gamble, your father, well*—she would point to various items in the house, as if I could just fill in the blank. What did we call what he did?

Together we picked up the broken objects on the floor: a cuckoo clock, a picture of her sister in a shattered frame, crystal candies spilled from a broken Murano bowl. As we picked up each piece, she would tell me where it came from as if we were archeologists examining someone else's ruins.

I got this at a garage sale, she said, handing me the biggest piece of the broken Murano bowl. *I paid $15.00. That was a good deal. You would pay at least $65.00 for that in the store.* She nodded once, emphatically, and I nodded back in agreement, then threw the glass in the trash.

We don't have antiques in our home that mean anything. Everything we buy is a good deal from a garage sale or a thrift shop. Everything we own is someone else's past.

Mom, I said, when I was younger and one of her good deals ended up in my room. *I hate this picture. This is my room. You can't decorate it without asking me. And look at this frame; there's a chip in it. It wasn't such a good deal after all, was it?*

Oh well, she'd said, putting it back on my dresser. *What do you expect? Nothing is perfect.*

Wish List

Had I been my mother, I would have told me these five things:

1. You won't beat your own child;

2. You will finally believe you weren't adopted, but you'll still wish you had been;

3. You will always wait for the other shoe to drop—sometimes it will

4. Sometimes it won't

5. You won't be able to control it either way.

TANYA KO HONG

The Crying Game

November outside Saratoga Springs / over coffee at the Red Roof Inn you say, *We're leaving for Florida* / snapshots cross my mind / race cars crash on a track / *No*, my voice shakes into a laugh / shocked by answer / hurricane fists and broken glass / I catch the danger in your eyes / *Eleven minutes, we're leaving* / you slam the bathroom door / I grab your .38 / from the nightstand drawer / next to Gideon's Bible / nudge the door open / shaving cream all over your face / our reflection / I point the gun / the back of your head / in this moment / we're young / again / think I'm pathetic / I smile / No more spaghetti sauce burning my skin / No more black eyes / No more three a.m. knife / at my throat / No more broken nose / after the football game / No more muffled screams / I fire / I didn't mean to shoot you / five times / but the gun only had five bullets /

E PENNIMAN JAMES

for Ron Athey

they came to watch him bleed

but he showed them his brain instead
playing hopscotch with a pistol
he removed his toupee
the contents were on display
thought projections carefully worded
from his soapbox in George Bataille's bathrobe
off with my head he cried
adjusting a voluminous set of horns
glasses discarded
lid flipped
he donned the royal wighat
white powder
a very sharp blade
you can't talk your way out
Japanese chrysanthemum
head on a platter
intestinal fortitude
day-glo anus
touch it with a ten foot pole

SB STOKES

ROOM STILL AVAILABLE?!??

I'm a guy who is looking for somewhere to lay my weary, wary head at night in this miserable city. The room you advertised sounds like such a spot. Like a good one, I mean. Yeah.

I can be described as clean, precise, articulate, nice (when sober, usually), artsy, fun, nasty, compact, lovely, fearsome, and laughable. My hair is baby fine and my jeans are all black.

I have no living pets and will only bring boxes full of toys and skulls into your abode, once invited to cross your threshold.

I have no known curses or hexes on me at this time and have been known to sing sea shanties in the shower during my "hour of power," which happens infrequently.

I will probably eat all of your foods, but know that in my heart they were mine— my foods!!!—not yours, so quit your whining already.

I am the person you want to be at home when you're not, or when you are. I love touching other people's underwear, but only in their drawers.

I am the one person you will want to give a rent discount to because I smell good and my teeth aren't fake. They are not mine, but THEY ARE REAL TEETH.

I am fond of being nude in both public and private, but promise not to leave pubes anywhere but the designated areas we agree upon, once I get you the stacks of hundos required before I can call you "roomie" to your face (and other things behind your back.)

I am deeply in love with you, even though we haven't yet met.

Believe me when I say, you want me to live with you right now. YOU WANT ME.

I hope to hear back from you soon, re: the room you posted online, which is currently available, and which you will rent to me ASAP for less than your asking price, Fucker. J/K

ZAC CAHILL

Kitchen Counter

Husband,

help me down
off our stainless steel appliances and
get me into my oven mitts. Husband,

I'll drink you under the table again and
chase you around
on all fours
like a lion—bite some calves,
bump my head. Husband,

bring a chair into the kitchen.
I am giving you a haircut
while this bread cools.

CAROL DORF

Categorize the Category of Categories

She's on her way out of the box, despite darkness,
despite shouts of *rootless cosmopolite*.

Naked, well that could be a problem, but let us assume
a silk dressing gown, or better yet jeans and a silk shirt.

You have to admit that being perfect is not always
a gift for the given. Open your eyes already.

        ...

You would think game theory referred to games
but the wiki-article refers first to battles.

Give me the problem of crossing Königsberg
bridges any day, perambulating afternoon.

        ...

When he asks her for a light in a post-code
movie, you know what he wants.

Sometimes they show her slapping his face
but the antecedent seems so mild.

How was it that the casting couch
moved from metaphor to joke to outrage?

In Hollywood your friends stab you in the front.
Why bother to hang a shmata to dry in the sun?

Retaliation can be shifty—
Did you know what he could be like, before?

                    ...

This isn't my story, and I wasn't consulted
which is right in the way of distant friends.

Opinions, and more, like any woman worth her salt
I have them. Luckily there are recitatives to fill the space.

Do you still drink milk? Cream? Sugar? Something sweet?
Let me tell you, *Life is Nothing Without a Plan.*

                    ...

The word *substance* when the sun sets in a green flash.
Imagine the random walk, the encounter.

Say, *He's my type*, and you fracture the world
separating possibilities into simple code.

Demonstrate *your type* is an abstract concept.
Sometime you identify *your type* as alien.

                    ...

She printed a board and fashioned pieces out of clay
for her lover to put into motion.

She opens and closes the doors, not here, not there.
Once someone said, *What are you looking for?*

Drapery hides darkness or light. Which will it be?
Beneath drapery lies expectation—cloth on cloth.

Intimate snap, she holds a terrier on her lap.
She's jealous of the nudes though she knows they are art.

You can see that enough is never enough, she said.
Maybe she was right but who carries the measuring cups?

...

Pleasure focuses on the instant and doesn't worry.
Pleasure does not read the paper or anyone's tweets.

ROBERT GIBBONS

The Dead Lecturer

For some it is not all racial, but spatial when I
cruise the corners of the Village in search
of the muse, swap poems for the dirge
in the bottom of the Yippie Café, and I saw the
beehive as historic as the Black Panther Party.

I saw Hettie and the five floor walk-up,
the dream deferred in between the storefront
and the liquor store, the gay club with all its
muse that will never be quiet, the storied
imagination as broadside and the perturbation.

The disturbance is my attraction, we studied
at the library on fifth, and people call him racist and
anti-Semitic, but people listened to eight track
tapes then, they listened to CDs, talked about
O'Hara taking long trips to Mexico, Ginsberg's
infatuation with toilet paper.

This is solitary. This is the only life that
one set of eyes can see. Only live once
then the afterlife, then the blues people
the yugen, the bluesology, the black dada
nihilist. He witnessed the junkie Christ twice
crucified with his rape of the trope, call him
experimental. Call him a chain gang.

A rope hangs his neck like a lynching. They were
no black poets on Broadway. If there were, take all
of them in their package down South. Then they
may become reborn. Come back and search for
their fame. IF they really want their words heard

then take construction paper, and crayons, take
tape and staple them to their body, pass them
like the subway poet, if his words are too academic
or too bluesy, then this is not good enough, say he
was an intellectual. I say,

he was six forms in one dark body.

JOHN PAUL DAVIS

Zero

Zilch, zip. The first word for nothing
in history is an Egyptian homonym for *beautiful*
—imagine if we started counting
there: beautiful, one, two, three. Zeno
asked, since we can't hear a single grain
of rice's impact when dropped,
how can that emptiness add up to the thunder
of a billion raining down into a silo?
Nil, nada, nought, aught, ought.
We draw an open mouth & it means one
less than one. In life but not in math
it also means two less than one
& three & so on til always.
In accounting it usually means the balance
of my checking account 15 minutes
before payday. In war
it means finding the target
& in the grocery it means calibrating
the scale. In Celsius, it means ice
& in Fahrenheit it means frostbite.
In gym class it meant I was the guy
picked last for every team. Sanskrit
named it after a desert & the Arabs translated
that as *sifr*, meaning *cipher*,
what we don't know, & Europe heard *zephyr*,
the wind blowing from the west

mangled by the English into the word
we use to mean the numeral shaped like an egg
before it hatches. Aristotle observed
there was no original egg without a bird
to lay it & no unhatched first bird
but fried chicken and omelettes
came from somewhere. The religious
believe a god must have laid the primal ovum
& scientists start with an explosion
or rather they start with the entire universe
condensed to the size of a grain of rice
then coughing outward forever
& that grain's origin is unknown
but believed to have been nothingness
meaning all things came
from the most unpromising
beginning, meaning if you have an empty
page you have everything, already
you have the knife-throw, heartache, exhale
& already you have the music
so begin: *beautiful*,

CONTRIBUTORS

DANIEL ARISTI was born in Spain. He now lives and writes in Switzerland with his wife and two children. Daniel's work is forthcoming or has been recently featured in *Salt Hill*, *decomP*, *Temenos Journal*, and *Blood Orange Review*. His chapbook *Familya* is published in 2019 by BPL Press.

OLIVER BAER is the author of the poetry collection *Baer Soul*. His writings can be found in *Axel: Metal Messiah The Underground Jeweler*, *Horror Writers Association Poetry Showcase Vol. II*, *Cthulhu Sex Magazine*, *Hell's Bells: Wicked Tunes, Mad Musicians, and Cursed Instruments*, and *Hell's Heart:15 Twisted Tales of Love Run Amok*.

DEMISTY D. BELLINGER's writing has appeared in many places, including *Necessary Fiction*, *The Rumpus*, and *Blue Fifth Review*. Her chapbook *Rubbing Elbows* is available from Finishing Line Press. Besides writing, DeMisty teaches creative writing, women's studies, and African American studies. She lives in Massachusetts with her husband and twin daughters.

GUY BIEDERMAN is the author of *Soundings and Fathoms* (Finishing Line Press). He has won awards in *Exposition Review*'s Flash 405 contests, and his stories and poems appear in journals such as *Carve*, *Flashback Fiction*, and *Sea Letter*. Guy hosts *This Day Afloat* on Radio Sausalito, lives on a houseboat with his wife and two mutinous cats, and walks the planks daily.

THOM CAGLE is a native of Nashville and a graduate of Temple University in Philadelphia where he studied poetry with Henry Braun. In Los Angeles, he has studied poetry with Laurel Ann Bogen, and he is also a proud alumni of the long-running Wednesday night poetry workshop at Beyond Baroque in Venice, California. Thom currently makes his home in Santa Monica.

ZAC CAHILL is a recent graduate of Alma College and lives in Michigan. His work has been published in *Gravel*, *West Texas Literary Review*, and *Aji Magazine*.

BILLY CANCEL is a poet/performer and sound/collage artist. His work has appeared in *Boston Review* and *PEN America*. His poetry collection *MOCK TROUGH RASPING CROW* is published by BlazeVOX. He lives in Brooklyn with his wife Thursday Fernworthy (Lauds) and together they perform as the noise-poetry duo Tidal Channel.

NEELI CHERKOVSKI was born in Los Angeles. He is the author of numerous books of poetry, including *Animal* (1996), *Leaning Against Time* (2005), *From the Canyon Outward* (2009), and *The Crow and I* (2015). He is the co-editor of *Anthology of L.A. Poets* (with Charles Bukowski) and *Cross-Strokes: Poetry between Los Angeles and San Francisco* (with Bill Mohr). In addition, Neeli has written biographies of Lawrence Ferlinghetti and Charles

Bukowski, as well as the critical memoir *Whitman's Wild Children*. His papers are held at the Bancroft Library, University of California, Berkeley. Neeli received the 2017 Jack Mueller Poetry Prize awarded at the Jack Mueller Festival in Fruita, Colorado. He has lived in San Francisco since 1974.

DOUGLAS COLE has published five collections of poetry and a novella. His work has appeared in publications including *Chicago Quarterly Review*, *Galway Review*, *Two Thirds North*, *Chiron*, *Pinyon Review*, *Confrontation*, *Red Rock Review*, and *Slipstream*. He has received the Leslie Hunt Memorial Prize in Poetry and the Best of Poetry Award from Clapboard House.

BRITTNEY CORRIGAN was raised in Colorado but has called Portland, Oregon, her home since 1990. She holds a degree from Reed College, where she is also employed. Brittney's poems have appeared in numerous journals and anthologies and she is the author of the collection *Navigation* (The Habit of Rainy Nights Press) and the chapbook *40 Weeks* (Finishing Line Press). Her current manuscript is a collection of persona poems in the voices of daughters of various characters from folklore, mythology, and popular culture.

ADINA DABIJA is a writer, philosopher, and western esoteric arts practitioner, currently living in New York. Born in Romania, she has published several books of poetry and fiction. Her first book, *poezia-papusa*, was awarded the Bucharest Writers' Association Guild Prize and her second book, *Stare nediferentiata*, won the Tomis Award. *Beautybeast*, from NorthShore Press, is her first poetry collection appearing in English. Since 2001 she has worked as an editor for *Respiro*.

Poet/collagist **STEVE DALACHINSKY** was born in Brooklyn after the last big war and has managed to survive lots of little wars. He is the recipient of an Acker Award for poetry, a PEN Oakland National Book Award, and in 2014 was honored with a Chevalier de l'Ordre des Arts et des Lettres by the French Minister of Culture. *Where Night and Day Become One: The French Poems* (great weather for MEDIA, 2018) was a silver prizewinner at the 2019 IBPA Benjamin Franklin Awards. Dalachinsky's audio CDs include *The Fallout of Dreams* with Dave Liebman and Richie Beirach, and *ec(H)o-system* with the French art-rock group The Snobs.

JOHN PAUL DAVIS was born in Durham, North Carolina, and has lived in Chicago, Ohio, San Francisco, and New York City. He is a graduate of East Carolina University and DePaul University. His writing has appeared in numerous journals and anthologies, including *Word Riot*, *The Journal*, *MUZZLE Magazine*, *Rattle*, *Four Way Review*, and *Bat City Review*. His first poetry collection *Crown Prince of Rabbits* was published by great weather for MEDIA in 2016. John Paul lives with his wife in New York City, where he works as a web developer, makes music and visual art, and writes poems.

DANIEL DISSINGER is a member of the Writing Program at USC. As a Kerouac and Beat studies scholar, he earned his Ph.D. and MA from Saint John's University, as well as an MFA from The Jack Kerouac School of Disembodied Poetics at Naropa University.

CAROL DORF is the author of the chapbooks *Some Years Ask* and *Theory Headed Dragon*. Her poetry appears in *Bodega, About Place, Glint, The Mom Egg, Surreal Poetics, The Journal of Humanistic Mathematics, Scientific American*, and *The Other Side of Violet* (great weather for MEDIA). She is poetry editor of *Talking Writing* and teaches mathematics in Berkeley.

MERRIDAWN DUCKLER is a poet and playwright from Portland, Oregon, and author of *INTERSTATE* from dancing girl press. Recent work can be found in *Ninth Letter, Pithead Chapel, Queen Mob's Tea House*, and the anthologies *Climate of Opinion: Sigmund Freud in Poetry* and *Weaving the Terrain: 100 Word Southwestern Poems* (Dos Gatos Press). Fellowships and awards include NEA, Yaddo, Southampton Poetry Conference, and Horned Dorset Writers Colony. Merridawn is an editor at *Narrative* and at the philosophy journal *Evental Aesthetics*.

ALEXIS RHONE FANCHER is published in *Best American Poetry 2016, Verse Daily, Plume, Rattle, Nashville Review, Cleaver*, and elsewhere. She is the author of four books of poetry, including *Junkie Wife* (Moon Tide Press, 2018), and is poetry editor of *Cultural Weekly*.

SARAEVE FERMIN is a performance poet and epilepsy advocate from northeast New Jersey. She has performed for both local and national events, including the Women of the World Poetry Slam, and the Epilepsy Foundation of Greater Los Angeles Care and Cure Benefit to End Epilepsy in Children. Her work can be found in *GERM Magazine, Drunk in a Midnight Choir*, and *The Careless Embrace of the Boneshaker* (great weather for MEDIA). She is the author of *You Must Be This Tall to Ride* (Swimming with Elephants Publishing) and *View From the Top of the Ferris Wheel* (Clare Songbirds Publishing House). Her latest collection *Trauma Carnival* (Swimming with Elephants Publishing) was published in 2019. She believes in the power of foxes and self-publishing.

RICO FREDERICK is a graphic designer and the author of *Broken Calypsonian* (Penmanship Books). He holds an MFA in Writing from Pratt Institute, is a Poets House Emerging Poets Fellow, a Cave Canem Fellow, and the first poet to represent all four original New York City poetry venues at the National Poetry Slam. Rico is a Trinidadian transplant, lives in New York, loves gummy bears, and scribbles poems on the back of maps in the hope they will take him someplace new.

JOAN GELFAND is the author of *You Can Be a Winning Writer: The 4 C's of Successful Authors* (Mango Press), three volumes of poetry, and an award-winning chapbook of short fiction. Joan's novel set in a Silicon Valley startup is forthcoming from Mastodon/C&R Press. Recipient of numerous awards and honors, Joan's work appears in the *Los Angeles Review of Books, Prairie Schooner, Toronto Review, Marsh Hawk Review, Kalliope, Rattle, Levure littéraire*, and many other journals.

CHRISTIAN GEORGESCU's tongue-twisting, pill-popping, foot-stomping work, *House of Me*, tours the human condition from the floorboards of depravity to the chandeliers of the soul. As a new member of the Poetry Brothel lineup, Christian will happily give you a poetry lap dance. For a fee.

ROBERT GIBBONS received his MFA in Creative Writing from City College in 2018. He has been published in journals including *Promethean, Killer Whale, Suisun Valley Review, Turtle Island Quarterly, Brooklyn Poets*, and *Fruita Pulpa*. His first collection, *Close to the Tree*, was published in 2012 by Three Rooms Press. Robert's chapbook, *You Almost Home, Boy*, was published by Harlequin Press in 2019. His next chapbook, *Flight*, is due out in the fall of 2019.

ISA GUZMAN is a Títere Poet from Los Sures, Williamsburg, Brooklyn. Dedicated to exploring the traumas and hardships of his Puerto Rican community and society at large, his work has been featured in publications such as *The Bridge* (Brooklyn Poets), *Acentos Review, La Casita Grande, The Good Men Project*, and *The Other Side of Violet* (great weather for MEDIA). Isa is currently pursuing his MFA at Brooklyn College. You can also hear him speak on the subject of masculinity and the Puerto Rican community on the podcast *Pan Con Titeres*.

JANET HAMILL is a "neo-Surrealist" writer and the author of eight collections of poetry and short fiction including, *Real Fire, Knock, Tales from the Eternal Café, Body of Water*, and *Nostalgia of the Infinite*. In collaboration with the bands Moving Star and Lost Ceilings, she has released the CDs *Flying Nowhere* and *Genie of the Alphabet*. Janet is the director of Megaphone Literary Arts at the Seligmann Center in Sugar Loaf, New York.

AIMEE HERMAN is a Brooklyn-based queer writer and educator with two full-length books of poems, *meant to wake up feeling* (great weather for MEDIA) and *to go without blinking* (BlazeVOX books), and a novel *Everything Grows* (Three Rooms Press, 2019). In addition, Aimee's work is widely published in journals and anthologies including *BOMB, cream city review*, and *Troubling the Line: Trans and Genderqueer Poetry and Poetics* (Nightboat Books). Aimee is a founding member of the poetry band Hydrogen Junkbox.

NGOMA HILL is a performance poet, multi-instrumentalist, singer/songwriter, and paradigm shifter, who for over fifty years has used culture as a tool to raise socio-political and spiritual consciousness through work that encourages critical thought. A former member of Amiri Baraka's The Spirit House Movers and Players and the contemporary freedom song duo Serious Bizness, he weaves poetry and song that raise contradictions and searches for a solution to a just and peaceful world. Ngoma was selected as the Beat Poet Laureate of New York for 2017 by The National Beat Poetry Foundation. *Conversation with Esu*, his latest CD, features poetry, jazz, funk, reggae, and blues.

AMY HOLMAN is the author of *Wrens Fly Through This Opened Window* (Somondoco Press) and four chapbooks. Recent poems have appeared in *The Ekphrastic Review, The 5-2: Crime Poetry Weekly*, and are forthcoming in *Gargoyle* and *Westchester Review*.

JULEIGH HOWARD-HOBSON's poetry has appeared in *The Comstock Review, L'Éphémère, The Lyric, Anima, Weaving The Terrain* (Dos Gatos Press), *The Nancy Drew Anthology* (Silver Birch Press), *The Literary Whip* podcast, and other venues. An English ex-pat, Juleigh now lives in the Pacific Northwest by a deep dark forest full of buried stars and secret whispers.

MATTHEW HUPERT is a writer and multi-media artist. He is the founder of the NeuroNautic Institute and its associated poetry workshop and of NeuroNautic Press which just released his latest collection, *Secular Pantheism*. He is the author of *Ism is a Retrovirus* (Three Rooms Press) and several chapbooks, and his writing has appeared in numerous publications including *Midstream Magazine*, *Maintenant*, and *Sonnets: 150 Contemporary Sonnets*. When not writing, Matthew can be found cooking for his family.

E PENNIMAN JAMES is a poet and performer from Brooklyn. His work has been presented at many venues throughout New York City and internationally in Chile, Canada, Thailand, Vietnam, and throughout Europe. He has been a fixture on the Brooklyn jazz jam scene for the last decade, reading in accompaniment to improvised music by such artists as Donnie McCaslin (Black Star), David Cook (Taylor Swift), and Tivon Pennicott (Gregory Porter).

PJ JONES is a pediatric occupational therapist servicing preschoolers with learning and developmental delays. By her own admission, it's fun work with immeasurable rewards. The other half of her duel love is writing flash fiction and short stories. A transplant from Harlem to Brooklyn, she is a regular attendee of New York Writers Coalition and a co-founder of LOTP / Ladies Of The Pen—an intimate supportive writing group from which "The Bath" originated.

DEBORAH KENNEDY is an author and artist whose recent book, *Nature Speaks: Art and Poetry for the Earth*, combines illustrations and poetry focusing on the ecological themes of our time. The book's honors include the 2016 Eric Hoffer Poetry Book Award and a 2017 Silver Nautilus Poetry Book Award. Her writing has appeared in *First Literary Review-East* and *Canary: A Literary Journal of the Environmental Crisis*. Deborah lives in San Jose, California, where she teaches college classes and poetry workshops. She often hikes in an urban riparian corridor where she spots osprey, hawks, and herons. In the evening she watches for moonbows, earthshine, and other modern miracles.

CRAIG KITE is a poet, musician, director of Mad Gleam Press, and slam champion of Staten Island, New York, which he represented at the National Poetry Slam. His work appears in various literary presses including *Fjords Review*, *Paris Lit Up*, *Maintenant*, and *The Opiate*. Craig has a background in journalism/human rights work and led field teams in Iraq in 2008-9. In addition, he has worked in Turkey, Chiapas, Guatemala, New Orleans, and Algonquin territory, Canada.

TANYA (HYONHYE) KO HONG is the author of four books, most recently *Mother to Myself: A collection of poems in Korean* (Prunsasang Press). Her work has appeared in *Entropy*, *Rattle*, *Beloit Poetry Journal*, *Korea Times*, *Korea Central Daily News*, the *Aeolian Harp Series Anthology*, *The Other Side of Violet* (great weather for MEDIA), and more. She is the winner of the Yun Doon-ju Korean American Literature Award, was a finalist for the 2018 Frontier Chapbook Contest, and holds an MFA in Creative Writing from Antioch University, Los Angeles. Tanya, who writes in both English and Korean, is an ongoing advocate of bilingual poetry, promoting the work of immigrant poets. She lives in Palos Verdes, California.

PTR KOZLOWSKI drove a lot of trucks and cars and cabs, set type in letterpress shops, and had to throw the drunks out when managing in a movie house. He was singing and songwriting and playing guitar in folk rock and new wave configurations, and writing poems along the way. Now he lives in Brooklyn and reads and performs around the New York City area.

CHRISTOPHER LUNA served as the first Poet Laureate of Clark County, Washington, from 2013-2017. His first full-length collection of poetry, *Message from the Vessel in a Dream*, was published by Flowstone Press in 2018. He has an MFA from the Jack Kerouac School of Disembodied Poetics and is the co-founder of Printed Matter Vancouver, an editing service and small press for Northwest writers. Since 2004, he has hosted the popular Ghost Town Poetry Open Mic in Vancouver, Washington. Christopher's books include *Brutal Glints of Moonlight, GHOST TOWN, USA,* and *The Flame Is Ours: The Letters of Stan Brakhage and Michael McClure 1961-1978*.

KATHARYN HOWD MACHAN is the author of thirty-eight published poetry collections, most recently *What the Piper Promised*, winner of the 2018 New Alexandria Press chapbook competition. Her poems have appeared in numerous magazines, anthologies, and textbooks. She is a professor in the Department of Writing at Ithaca College, emphasizing fairy tales. Since January 2011 she has written hundreds of poems about the shape-shifter Fox.

MIRA MARTIN-PARKER earned an MFA in creative writing at San Francisco State University. Her work has appeared in various publications, including *Istanbul Literary Review, North Dakota Quarterly, Mythium,* and *Zyzzyva*.

JULIAN née Sara **MITHRA**'s first book *If the Color Is Fugitive* (Nomadic Press, 2018) traces queer desire on the frontier of the American West and was a finalist for the 2019 Lambda Literary Award in Transgender Poetry. They eke out a living in Oakland encouraging young people to write.

ANTHONY MORALES is an Afro Nuyorican poet, educator, and activist who has been teaching for the past 20 years. His work has been featured in *Manteca!: An AfroLatinx Poetry Anthology* as well as various infamous street corner cyphers of trill repute. An urban birder, he wonders why we never learned we could fly.

TATYANA MURADOV was born in Moscow, Russia, and moved to a small town in Texas where she grew up. Since arriving in New York City seven years ago, she has performed in poetry events at Louder Arts, Urbana, Kiss Punch Poem, and KGB Bar. Tatanya's work deals with themes of immigration, love, and despair and has appeared in publications such as *Radius, Before Passing* (great weather for MEDIA), NYSAI Press, and JMF Chapbooks.

As a poet and essayist, **RICHARD JEFFREY NEWMAN** explores the impact of feminism on his life as a man. As a co-translator of classical Persian poetry, he writes about the impact of that canon on our contemporary lives. His most recent books are *For My Son, A Kind of Prayer* (Ghostbird Press) and the translation *The Teller of Tales: Stories from Ferdowsi's Shahameh* (Junction Press).

His poems, essays, and translations have appeared in a wide range of publications, including *Another Chicago Magazine*, *Prairie Schooner*, *Diode*, and *Unlikely Stories*. Richard is Professor of English at Nassau Community College in Garden City, New York, and curates the First Tuesdays reading series in Jackson Heights.

ANOINTING OBUH is an emerging writer from Africa. Her works have been featured, or are forthcoming, at *Isacoustic*, *The Cabinet of Heed*, *Barren Magazine*, *Honey and Lime*, and elsewhere. She currently studies English and Literature at the University of Benin, Nigeria. She says hello.

FRANCES OGAMBA desires freedom from something she is not quite aware of. She writes to find out. Her stories appear in the *Afridiaspora* and *Writivism* anthologies and online at *Enkare Review*. She lives in Port Harcourt, Nigeria.

VALERY OISTEANU is a writer and artist with international flavor. Born in Russia and educated in Romania, he adopted Dada and Surrealism as a philosophy of art and life. Immigrating to New York City in 1972, he has been writing in English for the past forty-five years. Valery is the author of over fifteen books of poetry, short fiction, and essays, including the poetry-collage collection *Lighter Than Air* (Spuyten Duyvil Press, 2017). He is also a contributing writer for French, Spanish and Romanian art and literary magazines. In addition, Valery exhibits his collages and assemblages at galleries in New York and collaborates regularly with jazz musicians.

JOSE OSEGUERA is a Los Angeles based writer of poetry, short fiction, and literary nonfiction. Having grown up in a diverse urban environment, Jose has always been interested in the people and places around him and the untold stories that each of these has to share. His writing has been published in *Jelly Bucket*, *The Inquisitive Eater*, *Main Street Rag*, and *Sky Island Journal*.

YUKO OTOMO is a visual artist and bilingual (Japanese/English) poet. She also writes essays, art criticism, travelogues, and more. Her publications include *The Hand of the Poet* and *STUDY & Other Poems on Art* (both from Ugly Duckling Presse) and *Koan* (New Feral Press). *Anonymous Landscape*, Yuko's latest collection, arrives September 2019 from Lithic Press. Her visual art, which focuses on the study of "pure abstraction," has been shown at Tribes Gallery, Anthology Film Archives Courthouse Gallery, ABC No Rio, Brecht Forum, Gallery 128, Vision Festival, and elsewhere. Yuko lives in New York City.

MARIO PONCÉ PAGÁN is founding member of the Títere Poets, a writing collective that explores the boundaries of masculinity, vulnerability, and male trauma. He is the guy in every boricua neighborhood that everybody knows: generally to be found on the corner, sometimes with other títeres, commenting on people, politics, the news, the hood rumors, the universe's mysteries, and stories from the past. Mario follows in the tradition of Capicu, Nuyorican, and Black arts movements. He is LaSopaNYC: School of Poetic Arts alum and his work has been published on *Sofrito for Your Soul*.

ANIA PAYNE lives in Manhattan, Kansas, with her Great Dane, two cats, and five backyard chickens. She teaches in the English Department at Kansas State University and her work can be found in *Sender Review*, *Punctuate*, *Panorama: The Journal of Intelligent Travel*, *Whiskey Island*, *The Rumpus*, and more.

DAN RAPHAEL's twenty-first book, *Manything*, was published by Unlikely Books in 2019. Recent poems have appeared in *Otoliths*, *Caliban*, *Mad Swirl*, *The Opiate*, and *Indefinite Space*. Most Wednesdays, Dan writes and records a current events poem for the KBOO Evening News in Portland, Oregon.

ERIK RICHMOND is a writer and musician from Chicago. His poems have appeared in the newspaper *The Long Islander*, in the journals *Ted Ate America* and *Medicinal Purposes*, and in the Chicago poetry anthology *In One Ear* which he also co-edited. He has lived in New York City since 1999 and performs regularly on the poetry scene.

ELLEN POBER RITTBERG's poetry and fiction have appeared in *Brooklyn Quarterly*, *Long Island Quarterly*, *Persian Sugar in English Tea vol. 1*, *Raw Ary Review*, *SlowTrains*, and many other journals and anthologies. A former journalist, her essays and features have appeared in the *New York Times*, *Huffington Post*, *Reader's Digest*, and other national outlets. Ellen's plays have been performed at festivals and Off-Off-Broadway, and she is also the author of the humorous parenting book, *35 Things Your Teens Won't Tell You, So I Will*.

SARAH SARAI's second poetry collection, *That Strapless Bra in Heaven*, will be published by Kelsay Books in 2020. Her poems are in *The Collagist*, *Golden Walkman*, *Ethel*, *Posit*, *Gone Lawn*, *Barrow Street*, *decomP*, *Oddball Magazine*, *Zocaolo Public Square*, *Sinister Wisdom*, and many other journals. Find her @farstargirl on Instagram or Facebook; or roaming Central Park in New York City.

G.G. SILVERMAN is a feminist author living just north of Seattle and is the daughter of immigrants. Her work has appeared in *The Other Side of Violet* (great weather for MEDIA), *Corvid Queen*, *So To Speak*, *The Journal of Compressed Creative Arts*, *The Iron Horse Literary Review*, *The Seventh Wave*, *Molotov Cocktail*, *Iconoclast*, *Ellipsis Literature & Art*, and more. She is currently at work on a short story collection as well as her third novel.

ALENA SINGLETON is a queer, brown, disabled, femme poet/writer who lives and loves in Brooklyn. A 2018 VONA poetry fellow, she was a featured performer with The Americas Poetry Festival of New York, the NYC Poetry Festival, Dixon Place, and at the Leslie-Lohman Museum of Gay and Lesbian Art. Her work has been published by *Sinister Wisdom* and The Operating System, among others, and is also part of "Viewfinding"—a public outdoor sculpture and queer poetry collaboration designed by artist Sarah E. Brook in conjunction with the NYC Parks Department.

JARED SMITH is the author of thirteen volumes of poetry, including his *Collected Poems* from New York Quarterly, and his fourteenth will be released by Spartan Press in 2019. His poetry and commentary have appeared in hundreds of journals and anthologies in the United States, Canada, Mexico, United Kingdom, China, and Taiwan over the past forty years. Jared served as a research executive in the public and private sectors, including as an advisor to several White House Commissions under President Clinton and as an advisor to Argonne National Laboratory. He now lives in Lafayette, Colorado.

PAUL SMITH writes poetry and fiction and lives in Skokie, Illinois, with his wife, Flavia. He believes brevity is the soul of something he read about once and whatever that something is or was, it should be cut in half immediately.

SB STOKES writes, draws, designs, and produces in the hills behind a lake in Oakland, California. His publications include a full-length poetry collection called *A History of Broken Love Things* (Punk Hostage Press, 2014), a chapbook entitled *DARK ENTRIES* (Gorilla Press / The Pedestrian Press, 2014), and a self-published chapbook called *Let's Call This Nothing* (2018). SB is one of the founding producers of Beast Crawl, an annual literary festival in Oakland which features over thirty readings and is 100% free.

MICHAEL SUTTON is a poet from Liverpool, England. He currently studies Creative Writing at Edge Hill University where he is the recipient of the 2018 Rhiannon Evans Poetry Award.

DENISE TOLAN is a writer and educator living in San Antonio, Texas. She has been published in places such as *Best Small Fictions 2018*, *Hobart*, and *Lunch Ticket*. Denise is obsessed with all things Moby-Dick and longs for calmer seas ahead.

MCKENZIE LYNN TOZAN writes in Chicago where she lives with her family and works as a copywriter, poet, and book reviewer. She received her MFA in Poetry from Western Michigan University, where she worked as the Layout & Design Editor for *New Issues Poetry & Prose*, and her BA in English from Indiana University South Bend, where she was Managing Editor for 42 Miles Press. Her poems have appeared in *Sleet Magazine*, *Rogue Agent*, *Whale Road Review*, *The Birds We Piled Loosely*, and *Analecta*, among others; and her book reviews and essays have appeared on *The Rumpus*, *BookPage*, *Memoir Mixtapes*, *Health*, and *Motherly*.

JOHN J. TRAUSE, the Director of Oradell Public Library, New Jersey, is the author of *Why Sing?* (Sensitive Skin Press, 2017), *This: For Your Eyes and Ears* (Dos Madres Press, 2016), and *Exercises in High Treason* (great weather for MEDIA, 2016). His translations, poetry, and visual work appear internationally in journals and anthologies, including *The Antioch Review*, *Crossings*, *Maintenant*, *Offerta Speciale*, and *Rabbit Ears: TV Poems* (NYQ Books). He has 120 turtlenecks in every shade thanks to Uniqlo and Dalton's.

For many years **SHARMINI WIJEYESEKERA** tried hard to drop out of society; she camped in urban parks, hitchhiked across Europe and played music for her dinner. Now she lives in London and writes to satisfy her wanderlust. Her poetry has been published in *Milvia Street* and *American Journal of Poetry*, and she also writes and records story-songs as the artist Charmed Life.

TAMIA WILLIAMS is a sophomore English and Communications and Media Studies double major at Washington College. As a double minor in Creative Writing and Journalism, Editing and Publishing, she spends her free time enjoying adventures in new books and attempting to build her own world through her writing.

FRANCINE WITTE is the author of four poetry chapbooks, two flash fiction chapbooks, and the full-length poetry collections *Café Crazy* (Kelsay Books) and the forthcoming *The Theory of Flesh* (Kelsay Books). Her play, *Love is a Bad Neighborhood*, was produced in New York City in December 2018.

ANNIE WOODS is an MFA candidate in Fiction at Wichita State University. She was a recipient of the Stephen C. Barr Fellowship for Creative Writingnand fiction editor of *mojo literary journal* in Fall 2017. She has been featured in *Hobart* and has upcoming publications in *A VELVET GIANT* and *Storm Cellar*. Annie currently lives in Denton, Texas. She likes to wear lipstick and spin in circles.

Founded in January 2012, **great weather for MEDIA** focuses on the unpredictable, the bright, the dark, and the innovative...

We are based in New York City and showcase both national and international writers. As well as publishing the highest quality poetry and prose, we organize numerous readings, performances, music and art events in New York City, across the United States, and beyond.

Visit our website for information about publications, submission calls, our weekly reading series, events across the United States and beyond, and to sign up for our newsletter.

Website: www.greatweatherformedia.com

Email: editors@greatweatherformedia.com

Twitter: @greatweatherfor

Facebook: www.facebook.com/great.weather

great weather for MEDIA titles

MORE

ANTHOLOGIES

Birds Fall Silent in the Mechanical Sea

Suitcase of Chrysanthemums

The Other Side of Violet

The Careless Embrace of the Boneshaker

Before Passing

I Let Go of the Stars in My Hand

The Understanding between Foxes and Light

It's Animal but Merciful

COLLECTIONS

melissa christine goodrum, *something sweet & filled with blood*

Steve Dalachinsky, *Where Night and Day Become One: The French Poems*

Michelle Whittaker, *Surge*

John Paul Davis, *Crown Prince of Rabbits*

John J. Trause, *Exercises in High Treason*

Wil Gibson, *Harvest the Dirt*

Corrina Bain, *Debridement*

Aimee Herman, *meant to wake up feeling*

Puma Perl, *Retrograde*

CPSIA information can be obtained
at www.ICGtesting.com
Printed in the USA
FSHW022133060719

9 780998 144061